The Global Sea

by HARRIS B. STEWART, Jr.

Chief Oceanographer
U.S. Coast and Geodetic Survey

A SEARCHLIGHT ORIGINAL

under the general editorship of

GEORGE W. HOFFMAN
University of Texas

G. ETZEL PEARCY
*United States
Department of State*

D. VAN NOSTRAND COMPANY, INC.
PRINCETON, NEW JERSEY
TORONTO   LONDON
NEW YORK

D. VAN NOSTRAND COMPANY, INC.
120 Alexander St., Princeton, New Jersey
(*Principal Office*)
24 West 40 Street, New York 18, New York

D. Van Nostrand Company, Ltd.
358, Kensington High Street, London, W.14, England

D. Van Nostrand Company (Canada), Ltd.
25 Hollinger Road, Toronto 16, Canada

Copyright © 1963, by
D. VAN NOSTRAND COMPANY, INC.

Published simultaneously in Canada by
D. Van Nostrand Company (Canada), Ltd.

Preface

Within the past two decades, much new information has been added to our knowledge of the sea. The next two decades should see much more. This book is an attempt to bring to the student and the general reader something of the fascination of the sea, a short summary of our present knowledge—including some results of recent studies in oceanography—and especially some feel for the influence that the sea exerts on our life today and the hope that it holds for our future.

The sea is many things to many people. To the commercial fisherman it is a sometimes calm, sometimes violent, but usually productive environment from which he derives his livelihood. To the mother of small children at the beach, it may be a terrifying thing of rip currents and pounding surf, an unknown menace to her offspring, a threat against which they have no defense. To the economic mineralogist faced with shortages of strategic minerals on land, it appears as a veritable treasure trove of untapped mineral wealth. To the artist and poet it is a never-ending source of inspiration, a thing of constantly changing beauty, at times restful and calm, but capable of fits of violence to try the souls of those who love her. To the scientist who studies her—the oceanographer—the sea is a magnificent addiction; once exposed to her complex interrelationships, once made aware of the sheer joy of learning her secrets, of exploring her vast uncharted reaches, he is a willing slave to the pursuit of more knowledge of her. To the average student the sea is what separates the lands in which he is more interested, for man has traditionally concentrated his activities on the lands on which he lives rather than on the sea that covers more than 70 percent of his planet.

Those of us who study the sea are still a relatively small but dedicated crew. We love the sea in all its moods. We are utterly fascinated by the many complex facets it presents to us: the unseen buried landscapes, the intricate movements of its waters, the abundance and almost unbelievable variation of the life it contains, and the amazing properties of that strangest of all liquids on earth—water. Above all, perhaps, we are most intrigued by the great potential that the ocean holds for the betterment of mankind. It is man's last great resource on earth, and the oceanographer is dedicated to obtaining the necessary understanding of the sea on which must be based its efficient utilization. The time has come to consider the ocean in its proper prospective, to realize that if we are to survive on this earth we must first understand the intricate workings of the global sea and the role this great body of water will play in the future of the race.

It should be made clear that the statements and opinions expressed are those of the author, and he alone is responsible for them in his capacity as a private individual. They do not necessarily represent the position of the U.S. Coast and Geodetic Survey nor of any other agency of government.

HARRIS B. STEWART, JR.

Washington, D.C.

Contents

Figures

1   *The Big Sea*

As MAN continues to break away from his Earth, as interplanetary travel becomes a reality and we earthlings are able to view our planet from the vast reaches of space, we will realize just how much of the earth is in fact covered with the waters of the global sea. In the meantime, however, we must rely for this information on maps or a globe. Our world maps are normally projections that show the continents in prominence and often tend to avoid showing the sea at all, or at most admit its presence almost grudgingly with a pleasant shade of blue. A globe, on the other hand, is seldom used because the ocean covers such a large percentage of the earth that a globe of any practical size has really very small continents, and none of the land detail in which we are normally interested can even be seen. Thus we have generally tended to neglect the sea in our geographical thinking of the earth. We have concentrated on the land areas where we live and build our cities, areas that are better explored and where the dependence of man on his physical world is better understood because the relationship is more direct and obvious. The land areas, however, are a relatively small portion of our planet. The ocean is tremendous. It is much too big for the small role to which we usually relegate it in our geographical frame of reference.

The total area of the earth has been calculated at 196,940,000 square miles, of which an area of 139,715,000 square miles—71 percent—is covered with seawater. We indeed live on a water planet, and on it the land and the sea are intimately related. The earth is a geographical unit of land and sea, and it should be considered as such a unit in our geographical thinking. This approach, however, will not be completely possible until we know as much of the sea as we do of the land. The land-sea interrelationship and man's dependence upon it are gradually becoming better understood as we learn more of the nature of the sea and the many fascinating processes that go on within it.

The study of the ocean has intrigued man's curiosity since the first primitive human stood on the shore of that early sea and looked off to the horizon and wondered—wondered where the waves came from, wondered at the regular heaving of the tide as though this watery monster were actually breathing, wondered at the strange forms of life that were cast up on the shore, and wondered what might lie on the other side. His successors over the centuries have amassed a large amount of knowledge of this sea. It has been a relatively slow accumulation compared to the rate at which we have learned about the land, but our knowledge has gradually increased.[1] It has not been a steady increase, but rather a series of pulsations. Periods of interest in the marine sciences have been interspersed with long periods during which little effort was directed to the study of the sea.

Now it appears that we are at the beginning of a marine "great awakening." The large maritime nations of the world have recently increased their support of the study of the ocean—oceanography, or oceanology as some call it. Many of the universities have initiated graduate courses in oceanography, and the previously small private marine laboratories are generally experiencing a long-awaited and welcome expansion. This increased interest is not limited to the United States, for the need for international cooperation in the study of the sea has recently been formally recognized with the organization of the Intergovernmental Oceanographic Commission under the United Nations Educational, Scientific, and Cultural Organization. From this present resurgence of interest in the ocean, it is

[1] The history of oceanographic discovery is well covered in *Founders of Oceanography and Their Work* by W. A. Herdman and *Searchers of the Sea* by C. M. Daugherty, both listed in the bibliography at the end of this book.

hoped that we will learn more of the ways in which man can utilize these 139,705,000 square miles of ocean for the betterment of his own lot on the mere 29 percent of the earth on which he can live.

2　*Important Facets of the Sea*

I̱F̱ I̱Ṉ ṮH̱E̱ P̱A̱S̱Ṯ we have been prone to limit our geographical thinking to the land areas, we have been equally guilty of thinking of the ocean as something other than a single world-girdling sea. Such phrases as "the seven seas" and "the oceans" imply that, in addition to the seven continents, there are several separate and distinct oceans or seas. The sea is, in fact, one global sea. The waters of each of the three major arms of the sea, the Atlantic, Pacific, and Indian oceans, intermingle in the vast circumpolar sea surrounding the Antarctic continent. (See Figure 1.) The marginal seas such as the Caribbean Sea, Bering Sea, Sea of Okhotsk, Japan Sea, East and South China seas, the Andaman, Arabian, and Barents seas, and the various mediterranean seas are merely smaller and partially enclosed arms of the same global sea.

There is really only one ocean within which lie all the continents and islands on which man has made his home. From this global sea have risen parts of the margins of his continental land masses and most of his islands. From this global sea the amphibian ancestors of man himself may have emerged during Paleozoic Time, and to this global sea man is being forced to turn for the food and resources to sustain himself as his numbers increase at an alarming rate. As President Kennedy stated in his March 1961 message to the Congress of the United States, "Knowledge of the oceans is more than a matter of curiosity. Our very survival may hinge upon it."

Why is the study of the ocean so important that the President of the United States should become this concerned about it? What can we hope to realize from the study of the sea that will be of

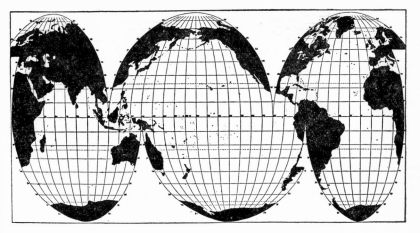

Figure 1. The global sea as shown on a special projection designed to emphasize the ocean rather than the land areas. Devised by Prof. J. Paul Goode, it is called Goode's Homalographic projection (interrupted) for the ocean. (From USC&GS Special Pub. No. 68)

sufficient benefit to mankind to justify the expense of outfitting ships and supporting oceanographic research and survey work?

THE CHALLENGE OF THE SEA

Probably the greatest enticement for those who today are devoting their lives to the study of the sea is the lure of the unknown, the challenge of the undiscovered, the thrill of discovery on what is truly the last frontier on earth. For years the challenge of the conquest of the Polar regions, the desire to plant a flag at the earth's poles, lured strong men to endure great hardships. Both the North and South poles have yielded to these men and their machines. Next it was the unconquered 29,028-foot summit of Mt. Everest that stood as the great challenge, but that too has succumbed to the indomitable will of hardy men. One by one, the few remaining unexplored regions of the continents, the few remaining "unspoiled" islands of the sea, have been visited by exploring expeditions. The motion picture camera and the articles and photographs in our magazines have made us all familiar with almost every corner of

the lands of earth. Only the ocean remains as the last great unexplored portion of our globe; so it is to the sea that man must
turn to meet the last great challenge of exploration this side of
outer space.

THE SEA AND METEOROLOGY

Although man's desire to search out the unexplored and to understand and explain the phenomena he discovers is the major challenge to the individual oceanographer, the sea holds much more
for mankind than the satisfying of the curiosity of those relatively
few men who recognize and accept this challenge.

Because of the high specific heat of water—the ability to absorb
and hold heat—the sea tends to act as a great thermostat to moderate
the earth's climate. It is this same property that makes the sea, in
effect, the flywheel of the earth's atmospheric circulation machine.
Yet we know relatively little of the interaction of the surface of the
sea with the bottom of the atmosphere. We know, of course, that
winds at the sea surface cause waves on the sea, but we are just
beginning to understand the quite complicated method whereby
this apparently simple phenomenon is caused. Perhaps the nature
of the air-sea interaction can be pointed out by a drastic oversimpli-
fication.

When the prevailing winds change direction, a change in the
ocean currents may result that may then move warm water into
an area of cool water. The movement of water, in turn, affects the
temperature of the air above the water. This change in temperature
then causes a readjustment in the atmosphere, resulting in a change
in the atmospheric circulation or wind pattern. This change in
circulation, in turn, affects the surface currents in the sea, and the
original current may be changed again. Thus there is an intricate
feedback mechanism between the sea and the atmosphere. Changes
in one cause changes in the other, but our fund of basic data on
the air-sea interface is still too meager to allow for anything other
than the most rash of speculations.

Our coverage of meteorological data over the land is now relatively complete. We are able to produce maps showing the distribution of the various weather conditions over most of the inhabited parts of the globe. As a result, meteorologists are able to predict the weather with some degree of accuracy over much of the land surface. This reliability, however, does not hold along those coastal areas where the prevailing direction of the wind is onshore, for there are few weather stations in the sea over which this coastal weather is made up. With meteorological stations now possible on less than a third of the earth's surface, it is little wonder that long-range weather forecasting is still in its infancy. As we learn more about the interaction of the sea and the atmosphere and are able to collect continuously the pertinent meteorological and oceanographic data at numerous points in the sea—perhaps from anchored or drifting buoys that telemeter their data to central collection points—we will then have the tools to help make accurate long-range weather forecasts. The economic potential of a system that would unfailingly predict the local weather as much as a year in advance is staggering to contemplate.

By the same token, this increased knowledge would provide the means whereby man could start planning on the modification of the earth's climate. Local climatic conditions currently make much of this planet almost totally uninhabitable. Climate control may indeed be the first great solution to man's continuing problem of the overpopulation of his land areas. Perhaps, to man, the most important interdependence of the sea and the land is through their interaction with the overlying atmosphere. Knowledge and eventual control of our weather demands a much more complete knowledge of the global sea.

THE SEA AND COMMERCE

For many years to come, the sea will continue to be the major highway for the exchange of bulk goods between the continents. Although we can hope to do little in the way of changing the sea as a medium for transportation, we can make our use of it more efficient as we understand it better. Within the last few years, for example, oceanographers have developed a system for forecasting wave conditions in the North Atlantic. Ships can thus be routed to avoid regions of rough seas, and costly ship time can be saved on the transatlantic run. We have just begun to explore the possibilities of nuclear-powered submarines. It is possible that much of our future marine transportation will be beneath the surface well below the depth of noticeable wave action. To prepare for this day, we must learn of the subsurface currents, which ones to avoid and which ones to utilize. Our maps of the ocean floor are adequate and accurate for only about one percent of the global sea, and this one percent is made up primarily of the relatively shallow landward margins of the ocean and the approaches to our harbors and estuaries. Organizations like the United States Coast and Geodetic Survey and the British Hydrographic Office have large-scale operations merely maintaining the existing coastal charts and expanding the coverage into uncharted or poorly charted coastal areas.

The condition of our maps of the deep sea, however, is about comparable to the maps of North America at the time of the Lewis and Clark Expedition at the beginning of the nineteenth century. There are landmarks on the ocean bottom that will, once they are charted, be as useful to the marine navigator as the Mississippi River, the Rocky Mountains, and other land features are to the aircraft pilot. Even now, transatlantic shipping uses as landmarks the prominent submarine canyons that indent the continental shelf on Georges Bank east of Cape Cod. Electronic echo-sounding equipment aboard these ships can tell the instant the canyon is crossed; and the maximum depth of the crossing, by reference to the chart, can be used to identify the exact spot at which the ship passed over the sloping canyon axis. This spot then provides an accurate fix of the ship's position. Georges Bank, however, is one of the very few places in the world where this type of navigation is possible, and it is possible here only because there are accurate charts available.

Even many of the major shipping lanes still are not adequately charted. On the run between the Panama Canal and Key West, Florida, the U.S. Coast and Geodetic Survey Ship *Explorer* in

1960 ran directly over—and then turned back to chart and sample—
an undersea mountain that rose abruptly from general depths of
nearly 1000 fathoms (6000 feet) to within 15 fathoms (90 feet) of
the surface. The mountain, although on one of our most traveled
sea lanes, did not appear on any chart of the area. Although this
undersea mountain, now called Explorer Bank, creates no hazard
to surface shipping, its implications for submarines are obvious,
both as a hazard and as a navigational landmark. The shape of
the sea floor has an importance to man in his commerce, and when
his advanced technology allows him to move large cargo-carrying
submarines at relatively fast speeds deep beneath the surface of the
sea, maps of the ocean bottom and of the subsurface currents must
be ready for him.

RESOURCES IN THE SEA

Man, in his typical wasteful way, has managed to consume his
natural resources on land at a rate that is already making him turn
to the sea as his last great relatively untapped resource on earth.
Approximately one per cent of mankind's food now comes from
the sea, and it has been estimated that the present annual rate of
about 40,000,000 metric tons of fish from the sea could be increased
anywhere from one and a half to ten times this amount. (A metric
ton is one million grams, or 2205 pounds.) That is, the sea offers
this large a potential catch. It is up to man to catch it. Today man
is a hunter of food in the sea, even as his ancestors were hunters
of food on the land. On land, however, he has by now learned to
raise livestock and to farm his fields. He has become a farmer
rather than a hunter. Not until he becomes a farmer of the seas,
until he is as well versed in "aquaculture" as he now is in agriculture,
will he begin to realize the great potential of the self-renewing food
resources of the global sea.

The primary non-renewing resources on land are our mineral
resources. Once they have been mined or quarried, there is no more.
It is the rapid diminishing of these mineral resources that is forcing
us to look to the sea for more. Petroleum, salt, sulphur, bromine,

and magnesium are already recovered in large commercial quantities from the ocean, but this list barely scratches the surface of the mineral resources that are dissolved in the waters of the sea and included in the rocks and sediments of the sea bottom. Manganese nodules have been found, by dredging and by bottom photography, to litter portions of the sea floor. These globular concretions, about the size of an average potato, have assayed high in manganese, nickel, cobalt, and copper—all essential metals in our present-day industrial complex. We know that they are there. We know that we will eventually need them, but as yet a practical method of recovering them is still in the thinking and drawing-board stage. The importance to mankind of the resources contained within the global sea will steadily increase as his supplies on land continue to dwindle. The basic research and survey work that will make possible the eventual maximum utilization of these resources must be encouraged and supported now. When we really need them, it will be too late to start learning. We will need to have the necessary knowledge already in hand.

THE SEA AND NATIONAL DEFENSE

Much of any future war will be fought over, on, and under the sea. As in any conflict, the side with the greater knowledge of the environment in which it is fighting has a decided advantage over the other. This statement was true when the Indians ambushed columns of soldiers from the protection of the American forests. It was true when the Philippine guerrillas tied up whole companies of Japanese troops during World War II, and it will be true at sea during any war in the future. For this reason, the navies of the world are busily trying to learn more about the marine environment. The major portion of this military effort in the United States is being carried out by the Naval Oceanographic Office, formerly called the Navy Hydrographic Office. The realization of the importance of oceanography for national defense has been one of the incentives for the present resurgence of interest in the ocean.

The global sea is a matter of great curiosity to the inquisitive explorer and scientist. It presents him with a real challenge. But the influence of the sea on man's daily life and on his future well-being is so great and still so poorly comprehended that the sea must be explored, studied, and understood so that it can be taken into account more intelligently whenever man pauses to think of his geographical setting. Geography is not so much man in relation to the land as it is man in relation to the whole of the earth on which he lives. The study of the sea is still in its infancy. By understanding the sea, we will better understand the interrelation of the land and sea and the nature of man's dependence upon this interrelationship.

3   *Buried Landscapes*

THE pleasantly undulating surface of the sea as seen from the promenade deck of a cruise ship gives not the slightest suggestion of the varied landscapes lying far beneath, buried by several miles of seawater. Not one whit more can be learned about these buried landscapes by looking out from the laboratory of an oceanographic survey ship. However, a ship of this type is outfitted with electronic devices for determining the shape of the bottom, so that the oceanographer has merely to stop watching the scenery and turn to watch the fathometer as it pings away relentlessly to produce a continuous trace of the sea floor directly beneath the moving ship.

This method involves bouncing a ping of sound off the ocean floor and measuring the time it takes to return to the ship. Previous to the development of this echo-sounding technique, the only knowledge of the shape of the sea floor was gained by the laborious —and none too accurate—method of lowering a weighted hemp line and later a thin wire from the ship and noting how much was needed to reach the bottom. Needless to say, even after many years of such lowerings, the shape of the ocean basins was known only in the most general way, and the details were not known at all. It was really the development of the continuously recording echo sounder in the 1940's that opened up the buried landscapes to exploration for the first time. Utilizing this equipment, a ship could steam continuously from New York to Liverpool and on arrival unroll a long strip of paper on which was recorded an unbroken trace of the depth of the ocean along the entire track. Some version of this basic echo-sounding set is now standard equipment on every

18

research and survey ship, and the precision survey recorders now being built enable the marine surveyor to obtain an expanded and detailed trace of the surface of the ocean bottom.

Such tracings, however, are of very limited value for mapping purposes unless the position of the ship is known at all times. It is of little use to know that there is a large undersea mountain somewhere between New York and Liverpool, unless you are able to pinpoint it on a chart. Although we now know a good deal about the undersea topography and have much of it generally located, it is only within the past few years that accurate long-range electronic navigation systems have been available so that a ship can know where it is with anything better than the two-to-five mile accuracy of the classic celestial navigation techniques.

Loran-C [1] is such a system, but it is costly to maintain, the shipboard receivers are expensive, and only a relatively small portion of the northern ocean is currently covered by this system. When satellite navigation becomes a reality, we will be able to make accurate charts anywhere at sea. This will be an era that oceanographers have long awaited.

MAPPING THE BURIED MOUNTAINS

Over the years, we have learned a good deal about the lands beneath the sea. We have sounded the deep oceanic trenches that contain the deepest known parts of the ocean. We have found countless isolated undersea mountains and some spectacular undersea mountain ranges. We have also found vast stretches of plains and some undersea channels that appear to be much like river channels on land. We know of the continental shelves and slopes that border our continental land masses, and we know the shape of many of the steep-walled submarine canyons that have been cut back into these continental margins. These are what we have found,

---

[1] The Loran-C system consists of powerful transmitters on shore which send radio signals to the ship from several stations. On shipboard, the time of arrival of the various signals, which varies according to the ship's distance from each station, provides an accurate "fix" of the ship's position.

but how were they formed? As the land geologist maps the shape of the landforms and samples the materials of which they are made in an effort to learn their origins and history, so too the marine geologist approaches the problem of learning the "why" and "how" of the buried landscapes his instruments reveal.

The problems of the marine geologist are considerably greater than those of his dry-land counterpart. He is unable to sit on the slope of an undersea hill and look out across the valleys and hills before him. He is unable to produce accurate maps from aerial photographs or decide where a critical rock or sediment sample should be collected and then walk over and pick it up. He must work above a topography he cannot see and obtain his samples by lowering pipes and buckets to collect his samples in what is really a hit-or-miss sort of way. His maps he can construct only by moving his ship back and forth above the bottom with his echo sounder turning out rolls of paper that must then be scaled and plotted on a chart and contour lines drawn to reproduce on paper the shape of the area he has been covering. It sounds like a long and arduous task, and in a way it is. But to those who make such things their business, there is a real thrill to sit at the front of a fathometer and "bring in a seamount," as we say. The problem would be quite analogous to mapping a mountain from a slow-moving dirigible flying at a constant altitude above the clouds that totally blanket the mountain, when the only instrument is an altimeter that gives a record of your height above the ground.

Aboard ship, sitting before the fathometer hour after hour, one becomes almost hypnotized as each swing of the stylus arm makes one more mark, extending by a fraction of an inch the trace representing the bottom of the sea. The sea floor has many bumps and small knolls, but to qualify as a seamount a rise must be at least 500 fathoms (3000 feet) above the surrounding topography. As the trace of the bottom begins each new rise, you wonder if this will be a big one. Oftentimes as the rise crests at something less than 500 fathoms, your curiosity is aroused; so after a hurried conference you turn the ship around and recross the feature on a parallel track but a mile or so away from the previous one. If you are lucky, you have turned in the right direction and now recross the seamount at a higher elevation than on your first track. This pattern continues until you have passed the peak. Since you have been recording the depth every minute or so during all of this tracking and have plotted the soundings along a track that has taken into account the various changes in ship's course, you now try to "hit the top"—to find the shallowest sounding. From your plot, you call the bridge and give them the heading that you feel will move the ship directly over the peak of the mountain. An ocean current may have been causing a continuous drift throughout this survey, but if you have run one or more crosslines, you should have a fair estimate of how much and in which direction you have had to adjust your lines in order to have exactly the same depth at the one point where two lines cross. This calculation gives an indication of the rate of ship's drift, and if you have cranked this additional variable into your estimate of the right course to take to "hit the top," you will probably do fairly well.

After you have gone through this procedure once or twice, it becomes a real game. There are numerous patterns that can be used, and there are good basic patterns dictated by statistics and by the theory of search. Most of us still, I think, would rather "play it by ear," that is, decide at the end of each crossing which way to turn more by intuition than by any preconceived pattern. The trenches and canyons of the sea floor are normally surveyed with lines spaced as closely as time and the accuracy of your navigational control will allow, but always the crosslines are necessary to correct for any drift of the ship due to surface currents or wind.

Most of our information on the deep sea has come not from the work of single oceanographic ships, but rather from a compilation of the soundings made along the tracks of all oceanographic ships that have traversed a given area. Very little of this sounding has been done on a systematic basis. The Gulf of Alaska is one exception. As the survey ships of the U.S. Coast and Geodetic Survey have each year moved from their Pacific base at Seattle to the working grounds along the many thousands of miles of coastline of Alaska and the

Aleutian Islands, each ship has moved along a different line. These lines have been carefully laid out in advance as part of an overall scheme to insure maximum coverage of the entire Gulf of Alaska. Holidays, as we call the unmapped areas between two adjacent lines, are frequently split with another track during a subsequent season. Even though, as one wit pointed out, you now have two holidays where you previously had only one, you do have additional information on which to base your contouring of the shape of the bottom of the ocean.

But what have these surveys revealed? How much do we now know of the shape of the ocean bottom and of the processes that have moulded its features?

OCEANIC TRENCHES

If the waters of the sea were removed, and we examined the earth from an orbiting satellite, without a doubt the most striking features we would see would be the great oceanic trenches. Comparable features are totally unknown on land, but the Aleutian Trench off southern Alaska paralleling the Aleutian Islands chain is deeper and broader than the Grand Canyon and would extend from Boston to San Francisco. The magnificent Tonga-Kermadec Trench lying northeast of New Zealand is shorter but deeper and can be partially visualized by imagining a trench seven times as deep as the Grand Canyon and extending from New York to Kansas City. The Research Vessel *Horizon* of the Scripps Institution of Oceanography working above this trench during Christmas week in 1952 measured a depth of just under 35,000 feet. Imagine, if you can, a hole in the ocean floor into which Mt. Everest could be upended and dropped, disappearing completely from sight and still leaving a mile of sea-water above it when it came to rest at the bottom. Such is the Tonga Trench.

The long, deep trenches are found only in the Pacific—if we can, for the sake of the discussion, consider the Java Trench as being along the margin of the Pacific. Their locations are shown in Figure 2. In addition to the Aleutian and the Tonga-Kermadec trenches,

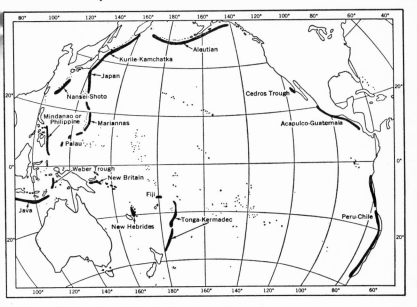

Figure 2. Trenches of the Pacific.

there is the Peru-Chile Trench lying close along the west coast of South America, where the drop from the crest of the nearby Andes to the bottom of the coastal trench is over 40,000 feet. Off Central America is the Acapulco-Guatemala Trench, but aside from this and the short depression near Cedros Island off the west coast of Baja California, Mexico, there is no great deep off the west coast of North America south of the Aleutian Trench. From there, the string of trenches is almost continuous around a third of the rim of the Pacific, with the Kurile-Kamchatka Trench, the Japan and Nansei Shoto trenches, and the Mariannas Trench, where the Bathyscaph *Trieste* with two men aboard went all the way to the bottom at 35,800 feet. The small Palau Trench is apparently a continuation of the Mariannas trend, and the Philippine, or Mindanao, Trench lies just east of the southern Philippine Islands.

The arc of trenches appears to split into two arms south of the Philippines, one swinging south and west through the so-called

Weber Trough south of western New Guinea, into the deeps off Timor and Flores, and on into the Java Trench that swings westward along the southern side of the island of Java. The other arm is considerably less continuous, but the trend of the New Britain Trench off northeastern New Guinea appears to continue into the New Hebrides Trench and possibly into the small trench recently discovered by the Soviet ship *Vityaz* north of the Fiji Islands. East of these is the great Tonga-Kermadec Trench, but no trench has yet been found across the broad southern stretches of the Pacific between there and the Peru-Chile Trench. Thus the ring of trenches is more of a horseshoe than a true ring. Very probably these trenches are limited to the Pacific margins, and none exists in the vast relatively unexplored reaches of the Pacific south of about 30° south latitude. This southern area between New Zealand and South America is the least known of the major portions of the global sea, so it cannot yet be said with certainty that no trenches exist there.

The deepest parts of the global sea are in these oceanic trenches. If past history is any indication, we have not yet found the deepest part of the ocean, for there is a steady succession of new "maximum depth" reports. For a number of years, the deepest known place in the ocean was the Mindanao Deep off the Philippines. Then, as exploration covered more of these trenches, it was found that the Mariannas Trench off the island of Guam was deeper. The most recent maximum depth reported for this trench is the 1959 depth of 36,204 feet reported by the Soviet ship *Vityaz* southwest of the island of Guam (at 11°21′N,142°12′E). For several years this remained the greatest known depth in the ocean. Then in the fall of 1962 the British survey ship *H.M.S. Cook,* while attempting to collect deep water samples in the Mindanao Trench, obtained a sounding of 37,782 feet east of the southern tip of the island of Mindanao in the Philippines (at 6°6′N, 127°25′E). Such deep soundings must have various corrections applied to them, and the data must be accurately checked before the sounding can be considered as a true depth, but it is quite probable that the official record will move from the Mariannas Trench back to the Mindanao Trench. The southern hemisphere record has been held by the U.S. research vessel *Horizon* since 1952, when she obtained a depth of 34,884 feet in the Tonga Trench. Probably deeper depths exist. It is just a matter of time before they are found.

Origin of oceanic trenches. The positions of the known trenches coincide very closely with the zones of the earth's most violent and concentrated earthquake activity. Nearly all the earthquakes of deep origin occur within the areas of the oceanic trenches. The ring of active volcanoes, the so-called "ring of fire," around the margins of the Pacific also coincides with these trench areas. Geologists feel that this is more than mere coincidence and that the active volcanoes, deep-focus earthquakes, and deep oceanic trenches are all somehow interrelated. The nature of the interrelationship is still in the realm of speculation, but it is just such speculation, such detective work on the global scale, that is part of the challenge of present-day marine geology.

Most probably the forces that produce the trenches are even now in action. The deep earthquakes might represent the release of tension built up by these great forces deep within the earth, and the volcanic activity would thus result from the reopening of old fissures and the occasional development of new ones through which the deeper molten material can escape to the surface. But what are these "forces" that cause all of this changing of the earth's shape? We really do not know, but we amass as many facts as we can, come up with a hypothesis that appears to explain the known facts, and then decide what additional facts we need in order to prove or disprove the original explanation. As new discoveries provide data that somehow do not fit the existing explanation, the original hypothesis must be modified. By the same token, there is the occasional thrill of discovering new facts that fit exactly the hypothesis currently in vogue.

The work on the Pacific trenches is a case in point. Current thinking is that these great trenches represent areas where the crust of the earth is actually being pulled down into the deeper, less rigid portion of the earth. This may seem like a fantastic idea at first, but consider the kitchen analogy of a large pan of water sitting across two burners on a stove, with each end of the pan resting over a burner. The warmed water at the ends will rise as it is heated, and the cooler water will descend in the middle until two vertical cells of moving water are formed. Surface currents are then moving from the ends of the pan across the top to the middle, where they meet and descend. Now assume that you cover the surface of the water with a layer of flour representing the crust of the earth. There will be a definite tendency for the flour in the middle to move downward where the two currents moving in from the ends meet and move downward. There will be a constant frictional force tending to pull the flour down in the middle. This force will be concentrated along the line where the tops of these two vertically moving cells meet, and there will be a continuous downward pull on the flour along this line and only along this line. This reasoning, when applied to the earth, does explain how the trenches might be pulled down, but it also requires that there be large vertical convection cells actively operating within the less rigid portion of the earth beneath the crust.

This was a new and an almost incredible idea when it was first proposed, but if it were true it would explain the origin of the great trenches. Then there was developed an ingenious piece of equipment called a heat probe. Lowered from a ship, this heavy probe penetrates the bottom of the ocean and measures and records the flow of heat upward from the sea floor into the overlying water. The obvious place to try out such an instrument was in a deep trench and on the relatively shallow rises well seaward of the trench. It is well known that in oil wells the temperature increases with depth as the warmer center of the earth is approached. Intuitively then, one would think that there would be higher temperatures encountered in the ocean floor at the bottom of a trench, which is several miles nearer the center of the earth, than would be found in the bottom on the more shallow rises far from the trenches. However, if the pan-on-the-stove idea, the convection cell hypothesis, were true, then you would expect that the warmer material would be rising to the surface under the shallower rises to give high heat-flow values, and the cooler material would be descending where the trenches were being pulled down and less heat flow would be found there.

The first lowerings in the Acapulco Trench and on the rise to seaward did show less heat-flow through the bottom of the trench. But these marine geologists are cautious. It could have been, they said, merely a difference in heat flow related to the fact that the measurements were made in two widely separated locations and not at all related to the trench and rise. It would take many more measurements before they could be sure. Over several years and several expeditions, the number of measurements of heat flow through the sea bottom has increased to the point where we are now sure that there is less upward flux of heat through the trenches. The Acapulco Trench, for example, has an upward loss of heat through its bottom which is less than half of the average for the surface of the earth. So in this case, the addition of new facts supported the hypothesis that their collection was designed to test, and the pan-on-the-stove or convection cell hypothesis is still the popular one used to explain the origin of these almost unbelievably large gashes in the bottom of the sea.

MID-OCEAN RISES

Undoubtedly, the oceanic trenches are closely related to the overall structural pattern of the earth as a geological unit, but we are just beginning to reach the stage where we have sufficient information even to recognize large-scale features in the earth's structure beneath the sea. As little as five years ago, the Mid-Atlantic Ridge running from Greenland to Antarctica and forming the backbone of the Atlantic was thought to be an isolated feature. Recent work, however, particularly by the marine geologists at the Lamont Geological Observatory of Columbia University, has shown that this is merely the Atlantic portion of a great continuous circumglobal range of mountains over 40,000 miles in length. The ridge extends into the Indian Ocean and through the eastern Pacific, actually "coming ashore" as part of the coastal mountain complex of western

North America. Over part of the length of this ridge, crossings with echo sounders have revealed a narrow median valley or rift, so this is a long mountain chain of global extent with a narrow valley running along the crest for at least some of its length.

In other crossings, there has been found a series of parallel ridges and rifts rather than just one major rift, and in still other crossings no depression at all has been found. Speculation is rife as to the cause of a feature of such magnitude. One hypothesis suggests that the earth is expanding and that this ridge-and-rift complex reflects the tensions resulting from this expansion. It is still much too early for anything other than the wildest of speculations, for additional work has shown that various segments of the worldwide chain of mountains have differing characteristics. Much of the chain still needs to be covered with reconnaissance surveys; none of it has been surveyed in accurate detail. Heat flow and gravity measurements are much too few, and few actual rock samples are as yet available for laboratory analysis and study. The discovery of this global mountain chain—or rather the discovery that the numerous previously known individual ridge systems were all part of the same worldwide system —is probably the most exciting discovery about our earth in the past twenty years. But this is a period of discovery in the global sea, and there have been other discoveries that will necessitate the rewriting of the classic texts in geology.

FRACTURE ZONES

Work of marine geologists at the Scripps Institution of Oceanography has shown that running essentially east-west across the floor of the eastern Pacific is a series of great cracks in the sea floor, which have been called fracture zones. All discovered since World War II, five of the nine now known to exist have been found within the past seven years. A typical fracture zone is more than 1000 miles in length and about 100 miles wide. Lateral and vertical movement along cracks, or faults, within these zones has resulted in long east-west valleys and troughs, and up through these fissures have poured the lavas to make some spectacularly large undersea volcanoes.

Typical vertical relief in these fracture zones shows differences of 10,000 feet between the tops and the bottoms of the ridges and valleys. The depth of the general ocean floor on opposite sides of the Pacific fracture zones often differs considerably, and the implication is that there has been a relative vertical movement of a whole segment of the ocean floor on one side of the zone.

Studies of the magnetic field across these features off California have provided information that is more than suggestive that large displacements of great blocks of the ocean floor have also taken place in the horizontal direction. The extent of these movements is amazingly large. The Mendocino fault, for example, is a prominent portion of one of these fracture zones. The magnetic evidence indicates very strongly that along 40° north latitude seaward of Cape Mendocino, California, the whole bottom of the ocean north of this fault has moved 750 miles to the west in relation to the area south of the fault. In the Atlantic, surveys are still too sparse to delineate comparable fracture zones—if they exist there at all. However, recent work by the Lamont Geological Observatory suggests that there has been some lateral movement along the ocean bottom seaward of the tip of Long Island. Perhaps, on further examination, this lateral movement will prove to be part of a fracture zone similar to those known from the Pacific, but we need more surveys of the sea floor, more information on which we can base and then test new hypotheses of the origin of our earth and the forces that have shaped its land and seascapes. We are just on the threshold of a new era of global geological theories, and it appears that the real clues lie in the structures to be found at the bottom of the global sea.

SEAMOUNTS

Many of the smaller structural features of the deep sea are no less intriguing. The undersea mountains, or seamounts, hold a special fascination for the marine geologist. They have been found in all major branches of the global sea. Those crowding the crest of the Mid-Atlantic Ridge probably make up the greatest concentration in the Atlantic, but there is a fine string of seamounts between Cape

Cod and Bermuda, and a recently published physiographic diagram of the Atlantic floor shows literally hundreds of these isolated peaks. Most of these undersea mountains appear to be volcanic in origin, that is, they are underwater volcanoes that now are dormant. Only rarely have these features been observed in the process of construction. Miojin Sho off the Japanese islands was one such undersea feature where an eruption was observed and photographed. The holocaust is well documented, but the price was high, for the entire scientific party and crew of the Japanese research vessel *Kaijo Maru* were lost when the ship was completely destroyed by a sudden eruption directly beneath it.

Obviously, some of these volcanoes have risen through the surface of the sea to become islands. The Hawaiian Islands are examples. Others have risen above the sea and then been reduced by the rasp file of the surf beating against their edges, to disappear again below the surface of the sea. Falcon Bank (formerly Falcon Island) in the Tonga Islands north of New Zealand is a classic example of this. Falcon Island has risen from beneath the sea and been cut back to sea level several times during the last two hundred years. When it was visited by the Capricorn Expedition of the Scripps Institution of Oceanography in 1953, it was again totally submerged, and corals had started anew to grow on the pile of cinder rubble.

This same process of erosion to sea level is the best possible explanation for the many flat-topped seamounts that have been discovered throughout the Pacific. First explored in detail by a Princeton geology professor who found himself as the navigation officer on a Navy ship in the Pacific during World War II, the features were promptly named "guyots" by him in honor of the eminent Swiss geologist, Arnold Guyot, who was long a leading teacher with the Princeton Geology Department. These flat-topped seamounts, or guyots, in general have the shape of a truncated cone, an almost perfect volcano shape but with the top neatly sliced off. These are not volcanoes that have "blown their top," as did the one in which Crater Lake now sits, for there is no crater on the top of any known guyot. In most cases, guyots are as flat as a football field, perhaps with a narrow, gently sloping outer edge between the flat top and the steeply sloping sides. Planation to sea level by wave action was the obvious explanation, but most of these flat tops are now several hundred fathoms below sea level. The question immediately posed is "If the tops were made flat at sea level, how did they become 'drowned' so far below the present level of the sea surface?"

A rise in sea level may have contributed to their submergence, but more probably the major factor was the depression of the sea floor by the weight of the seamounts themselves and by what the geologists call regional downwarping. Echo-sounding surveys have revealed that many of these large seamounts are surrounded by a moat-like depression, suggesting that the sea floor just was unable to support all that weight of volcanic rock. That downwarping of the ocean bottom also can contribute to the submergence of guyots is dramatically pointed out by a large flat-topped seamount just south of Kodiak, Alaska. The top of this guyot lies at more than 1000 fathoms (6000 feet) below the surface, considerably deeper than any of the many other guyots found in the North Pacific. The interesting fact here is that this is the only guyot found within the great Aleutian Trench. The implication is obvious that the seamount was carried downward by the downward movement of the trench itself, thus placing the top of this seamount well below the tops of all the others. This, incidentally, is additional evidence that the trenches are "pulled down" into the earth rather than having been cut as some might suppose.

CORAL ISLANDS

In the tropical areas where reef-building corals can flourish (between about 30° north and 30° south of the Equator), these flat-topped seamounts, while still relatively shallow, provided some of the platforms on which reefs became established. As the platforms subsided, upward growth of the reef progressed at a rate that kept the reef-building organisms within the sunlit depths where they could maintain reef growth. This mechanism may explain the development of some coral atolls such as Bikini and Eniwetok; but for others there is no known guyot beneath, and the Darwinian explanation of the upward growth of coral around the periphery of a sinking island appears to be the best explanation. Elsewhere, as at Falcon Bank, corals are known to become established on a submerged bank with no actual subsidence of the platform needed. In some other cases, there may have been no actual subsidence of the platform, but the organisms maintained upward growth as sea level rose.

The origin of atolls and other coral islands has been one of the great controversies of modern science. The four "D's"—Darwin, Dana, Davis, and Daly—made major contributions to the theory of the origin of coral islands, and the exploration of these intriguing features continues. Most probably it will be found that no sweeping theory can adequately explain all the atolls and other coral islands, but that each must be investigated separately to establish the method of its development. When many of these have been so studied, then we can begin to generalize.

CONTINENTAL SHELF AND SLOPE

Almost universally, the continents are bordered by a relatively shallow underwater terrace. The generally broad gently sloping landward portion is the *continental shelf*. The narrow, steeper outer slope where the terrace drops off to meet the deep sea floor is the *continental slope*. Coastal shipping is carried out over the continental shelf; in some areas petroleum is obtained from the ancient sediments below the surface of the shelf; much of the world's fishing is in the waters over the shelf; and the continental shelf will probably be the first area where commercial mineral recovery from the sea floor will be attempted. The continental shelf is the transition zone between the land and the deep sea, but even though it is the most available part of the global sea, only the inner portions of a relatively small part of it are adequately mapped.

On a world basis, the continental shelf averages a bit over 40 miles in width, with the average depth at the outer edge being about 70 fathoms (420 feet). The average slope from the shore to the outer edge is about ten feet per mile, being somewhat steeper on the inner than on the outer portions. The continental slope, on the other hand, though everywhere steeper than the gently sloping continental shelf, averages only about 400 feet per mile. Off southern Cuba, along what appears to be a straight fault coast, the continental slope in places is steeper than 45°, but this is the extreme exception. Actually, this is probably the steepest underwater slope of any large extent anywhere in the sea.

The origin of the continental shelf and slope is still unknown. At first, before they had been surveyed or sampled to any extent, the continental terraces were thought to be a large apron of sediments washed into the ocean from the land and built up over the ages much the same way the delta of a river is built up. This view led to the conclusion that if you sampled the sediments on the surface of this terrace, you would find the coarser sediments nearer the land, and successively lighter sediments would have been carried successively farther to sea, so that on the very outer edge there would be nothing but fine muds. This all made very good sense until oceanographers began to sample the shelf sediments. As has so often been the case in the study of the sea, the pat explanations dreamed up from the comfort of a couch ashore crumble like a child's sand castle on a rising tide once you leave the couch and go out to see what actually is there.

So it was with the early explanations of the origin of the continental shelf and slope. Not only did the sediments not prove to be coarse inshore and finer offshore, but the reverse was true in many areas. In others there was a most patchy distribution of fine and coarse sediments, and in many places actual outcrops of rock were found at the very outer edge of the continental shelf. Perhaps, one might suppose, these shelves were planed off by surf action the way the guyots were. However, the use of explosives to study the subsurface structure by bouncing sound waves off layers of hard rock beneath the surface of the bottom has shown that, at least off the Atlantic coast of the United States, there is a deep fill of sediments on the landward part of the shelf. Certainly this is not what would be found if the terrace were a feature due to erosion rather than to filling by sediments. Most probably the explanation is not the same for the shelf everywhere in the world. In some cases—particularly off glaciated coasts—erosion may be the main agent of shelf formation. Elsewhere, as off large river mouths, sedimentation may be the dominant agent. Probably a combination of the two processes, erosion and deposition, will in the end be the best explanation; but in the meantime, this feature is "free game" for anyone who wants to take all the available facts into account and come up with a hypothesis of his own.

SUBMARINE CANYONS

Cutting through the continental slope and back into the continental shelf are many truly spectacular submarine canyons. Speculation on their origin has been a major controversial topic in marine geology for several decades, and countless professional papers advocating one hypothesis over another have been published in the scientific literature. The fight still rages, even though the earlier ideas of submarine solution as in limestone caverns, scouring by undertows, erosion by artesian springs, and gouging by seismic sea waves ("tidal waves") have been pretty well discarded by all marine geologists.

The controversy now revolves around two diametrically opposed concepts. The first is that the submarine canyons are of primarily submarine origin, having been carved under water by fast moving sediment laden currents (the so-called turbidity currents). The other concept is that the canyons were basically formed above water at the time of a lower stand of sea level and are therefore essentially drowned land canyons. The facts marshalled by the proponents of each of these concepts are impressive, so impressive in fact that they are probably both partly correct, and the real answer undoubtedly lies somewhere in between. According to this intermediate view, the canyons originated at a lower stand of the sea as land canyons. As sea level rose, however, the only canyons that remained were those that were not subsequently filled with sediment, but were kept open and deepened by turbidity current action. This hypothesis is just as open to argument as are the others based on the same facts.

The origin of submarine canyons is another of the "free game" areas, a grand submarine geological squabble in which all who have the facts are urged to take part. New exploratory tools such as the deep-sea cameras, the newly developed equipment for determining the thickness of sediments over the basement rock, and self-contained diving apparatus are all capable of shedding new light on this old problem. Any day a wholly new concept may have to be developed to explain an entirely new set of facts derived from the further study of these canyons.

Regardless of how they were formed, the canyons themselves are most interesting. Seaward of the Hudson River, the Hudson Canyon swings southeast across the continental shelf and slope and has been traced 200 miles seaward of the base of the continental slope by the Woods Hole Oceanographic Institution's research vessel *Atlantis*. On the shelf, the canyon is steep-sided and quite similar to land canyons. Below the base of the slope, the shape is more that of an entrenched river meandering across the sea floor.

On the west coast of the United States, the Monterey Submarine Canyon is the most spectacular. Its head is just off the end of the pier at Moss Landing near Monterey, California. The canyon is quite similar in profile to the Grand Canyon, and over part of its length is over a mile deep from the lip to the bottom. The canyon winds seaward for 50 miles, whereupon the steep inner canyon gives way to a broader trough that terminates in a wide fan-shaped submarine delta. Across this delta, several channels with levee-like sides show a marked similarity to those of river deltas on land. The leveed sides of the channels, undoubtedly formed by overflow as are the better-known natural levees of the Mississippi River, are strong evidence for the action of turbidity currents. These sediment-laden currents moving out of the canyon mouth and across the delta have mixed with the surrounding water, and some of the sediment thus lost from the major stream of turbid water has been deposited along the sides as levees. Undoubtedly these coastal canyons act as great sewers to carry seaward sediment that is moved into their shallower heads by longshore currents.

Detailed charts prepared by the U.S. Coast and Geodetic Survey have been carefully contoured and used to estimate the volume of the sediment in the delta at the mouths of several of the California canyons. From these charts it was found that there is many times more sediment in the deltas than ever was removed in the mere cutting of the canyons themselves. This sewer action must provide vast quantities of the finer sediments that do not end up on the deltas, but are carried far seaward in suspension and added to the sediments of the sea floor at great distances from their point of origin.

Many canyons head offshore opposite the mouths of rivers; but just enough do not, so that we cannot generalize. Most canyons appear to be cut into relatively soft sediments; but just enough are cut into hard rock (Carmel Canyon off California is cut into granite), so that again generalization is not warranted. The one thing all submarine canyons have in common is an air of mystery, that same challenge of the unexplored and unexplained. Diving in the head of Scripps Canyon off La Jolla, California, at a depth of 100 feet, you can reach out both hands and touch the walls on either side of the steep, narrow gorge. Looking upward, you see the narrow slit far above that is the surface, and between you and the sunlit surface of the sea myriads of fish drift lazily as black silhouettes. It is indeed a fascinating world.

THE SHORE

To landbound man, the most significant part of the ocean floor is the narrow line where the bottom of the sea becomes the surface of the land—the shore. Here he comes for his holidays to sun on the beach and to swim, to launch his boats, to fish, or just to sit and marvel at the ever-changing patterns of sea and sky. Here also is where he locates his great ports, docks his ships, and builds his marinas and resort hotels. But here too is where he releases much of his sewage and industrial wastes, where he struggles to keep the sands from moving out and leaving his structures to collapse into the sea, or struggles to keep the sand from moving in and filling his navigable channels. The shore is an area of almost constant change due both to the catastrophic and to the less violent day-to-day processes that mold and shape the shorelines of the world. As man builds new structures along the shore and interrupts the natural processes in action there, the delicate equilibrium is changed, and erosion or deposition takes place as the attempt is made to establish a new set of equilibrium conditions. It is an area of constant change, but by the same token, one of continuing interest to the marine geologist.

How many times have people come to the beach in the early spring and commented on all the rocks that "came in" during the winter? On many of the world's sand beaches, the last swimmer of the summer leaves a beach piled high with clean sand only to return in the spring to find the surface covered with coarse cobbles. Were he to keep weekly records of the height of the sand against a seawall or an abandoned piling, he would discover that instead of the rocks "coming in," the sand has gone out and uncovered the cobbles that lay beneath.

The annual migration of beach sand on and off the shore has been well documented. The high waves resulting from the storms of the northern-hemisphere winters rush high on the beaches, put the sand in suspension, and carry it seaward with the violent backwash. This action continues until the storm-generated surf of the winter is replaced by the more gentle waves of the summer period. Under these new conditions, the sand in suspension is carried up onto the beach, but the more gentle waves have no violent backwash. Rather, they sink into the porous beach and leave their suspended sand as a new layer upon the surface. This replenishment of sand continues throughout the summer until the cobbles are covered and the beach is back up to its autumn level.

Of course, there are other cycles that affect the beach, cycles related to regular tidal variations in sea level, but these are considerably less than the annual cycle. One storm in the middle of the summer, however, can upset the whole balance by moving out within a few days large quantities of sand that the remaining months of summer are unable to replace.

There is nothing sacred about the present level of the sea. There are marine deposits laid down on ancient sea bottoms now left high and dry by a retreating sea and found over much of the earth. Sea level has also stood much lower in the past, as attested to by ancient shoreline features now found buried under hundreds of feet of seawater. Our shorelines today are transient things, and future generations will do their bathing and their ship launching along a shore far inland or far seaward of the present shoreline. The change is gradual and may be heralded by the occasional storm surges that bury low-lying coastal airports under several feet of water or flood out the New York City subway system. On the other hand, the change may first be signaled by a gradual but continued shoaling of the major harbors, necessitating increased dredging to maintain the waterways. The one thing of which we are most sure is that it will change. The questions that cannot be answered yet are when will it become a significant factor in our coastal life and which way will sea level be going then, up or down?

Nearly three quarters of the earth's landscape is buried beneath the waters of the global sea. Some of the features of these buried landscapes are almost impossible for landbound man to visualize. Even as they are shown on the laboriously constructed maps of the sea bottom, the landscapes generate more questions than they answer. It is to the sea that man must turn with his inquisitiveness, his ability to reason, his strength and perseverance, his ships, and his instruments to explore and study these buried landscapes. From these studies man can hope to learn many secrets of how the features of his earth were formed and perhaps utilize this knowledge for the betterment of his own lot and that of his fellow man.

4 *The Moving Waters*

THE global sea is in constant motion. Surface waves are perhaps the most readily apparent of these ocean motions, but how are they formed, how deep beneath the surface are they felt, why do breakers form, and what are "tidal waves"? The movement of the sea is also noted in the regular rise and fall of the tide and in the horizontal currents that are part of the tidal phenomenon, but what causes these, and why do they vary so from place to place and from day to day? What of the great ocean currents like the Gulf Stream? What is the global pattern of the ocean's currents, and what causes them? These are the questions that have piqued the curiosity of marine scientists for centuries. All of them have been partially answered—but only partially. We do not have the final answer to any of these questions. It is these very questions and the many others relating to the motion of the sea's waters that physicists and mathematicians find so challenging. The world's physical oceanographers are dedicated to finding more answers to the many intriguing questions posed by the complex movements of the waters of the sea.

WAVES

The surface of the sea is in constant motion. Waves are always present. These may be the gentle wavelets caused by the first puff of morning breeze that ripples the glassy surface of a quiet anchorage, or they may be the crashing surf generated by an offshore storm. Waves seem to hold an almost hypnotic fascination for man, and he has sung of them, painted them, and sat for countless hours mesmerized by their relentless advance upon the shores of his lands.

But man's curiosity has also been piqued by the ocean's waves, and there has been built up over the years a large body of knowledge concerning the waves present in the sea.

Wind waves are, of course, the most common. They include not only the waves built up locally by winds blowing at the time, but also the long gentle swell that rolls in on our beaches even when there is not the slightest breath of wind along the shore. These latter waves are the continuing effect of storms far at sea; and even as a pebble thrown into a still pond creates a wave train that reaches out far from the point where the pebble entered the water, so too these waves have often traveled many hundreds or even thousands of miles from the storm center where they were first created. The big long-period waves that make the surfing conditions so good along much of the southern California coast are usually the so-called "southern swell" that has been generated many thousands of miles to the southwest in the equatorial regions of the Pacific. In the Atlantic too, swells have been observed off the English coast that are known to have traveled from the distant South Atlantic.

Although waves at sea can be dangerous to ships, their most common effects are personal discomfort and the annoyance of having to slow down or change course in order to cross a region of troublesome wave conditions. Most waves in the open sea are less than 12 feet high. Waves between 25 and 50 feet in height are rare and are associated with only the most severe storms. Stories of monstrous waves at sea are considerably more common than the waves themselves, and few such stories have been well documented. The classic exception to this generality is the wave encountered by the U.S. Navy tanker *Ramapo* in 1933 en route from the Philippines to San Diego. She was running downwind with exceptionally large waves coming up behind her, lifting her high as they rolled underneath, and then dropping her down into the trough. At one point the watch officer on the bridge happened to make certain observations that enabled the geometry of the situation to be worked out to determine the height of the next wave bearing down on him from astern. Standing on the bridge and looking aft as the stern wallowed in the trough, the watch officer saw the crows nest on the mainmast momentarily lined up precisely with the crest of the approaching wave just after it had blotted out the distant horizon. This meant that the eye of the watch officer at that moment was just level with the crest of the wave, so that the vertical distance between the sea surface at the stern of the ship and the horizontal line connecting the viewpoint on the bridge with both the crows nest and the horizon must be equal to or smaller than the height of the wave. When the ship's plans were rolled out and the distances measured, it was found that the wave was at least 112 feet high. To this date, this remains as the highest wave at sea for which there is any relatively reliable measurement.

Man, however, is generally more concerned with the waves as they affect his coasts. This is also an area of great interest to the physical oceanographer, for this is the region where the direction of the deep ocean waves is modified by the bottom topography, where the mathematics of wave propagation changes, where the wave form is modified and breakers are formed, and where tremendous amounts of energy are released. To begin to understand what is taking place in this area where the waves approach the shore, it is necessary first to know the meaning of a few of the terms oceanographers use to describe waves.

Wave length is defined as horizontal distance from one crest to the next. The *height* of a wave is the vertical distance between the bottom of a trough and the crest of the next wave. The *period* is the time between the passage of one crest and the passage of the next one at a given point. The wave *velocity* is the speed of advance of the wave crest. Thus any simple regular train of waves can be described using only these four terms.

There are several questions about waves that are most commonly asked: how deep beneath the surface is wave action felt, why do waves break as they approach the shore, and why is it that the waves always seem to approach parallel to the beach regardless of which way the shoreline trends?

Depth of wave action. Anyone who has donned a faceplate and paddled along at the surface over a bed of seaweed has noticed how the seaweed beneath him flops back and forth in response to the waves. With the advent of the aqualung, divers are roaming all over the shallow bottoms of our coastal seas. They have noticed at depths of fifty and more feet that, if they stop swimming, they often are moved first one way and then the other by the action of the waves passing overhead. Submariners have also noted that once they are at depths of 200 feet, wave action is only very rarely felt. As a wave moves forward in the open sea, the individual water particles are moved upward and forward under the crest and downward and back under the trough, thus moving in a vertical circular orbit. This motion is nicely illustrated by a piece of floating driftwood that does not move forward with the velocity of the wave, but rather describes this circular motion of up, forward, down, and back as each wave moves under it. The diameter of this vertical circle at the surface is exactly the same as the wave height.

With depth, however, the diameter of the circular orbit of particle motion decreases rapidly, so that at a depth of half the wave length of the surface wave, the orbital motion of each water particle is only 4 percent of that at the surface, and wave motion is imperceptible at a depth equal to the surface wave length. The greatest wave lengths in the open ocean seldom exceed 600 feet. On theoretical grounds, at least, the motion at a depth of 300 feet for a 20-foot-high wave of this period would be only 10 inches.

Breakers. As a wave approaches the shore and enters shallow water, the character of the wave changes as it "feels bottom." What this means is that at a depth of water about equal to one half the deep-water wave length, the orbital motion of the water particles is impaired by the bottom, the orbits become eliptical, and at the very bottom only a back-and-forth motion results. As a consequence of this "feeling bottom," the wave velocity is decreased, the crest of the wave peaks up, and the particle velocity at the crest increases as the wave continues to rush toward the beach. Finally the wave becomes oversteepened, the top of the crest gets going faster than the wave, and the whole thing topples forward as a breaker. The wave has essentially been destroyed, and what is left is a mass of water rushing up the beach.

On the average, a breaker forms when the wave reaches water about 1.3 times as deep as the height of the wave itself. Thus along a gradually shoaling shore, the larger waves break farther out than do the smaller ones. It is this same relationship of wave height to depth of breaking that is of great assistance to the mariner operating in reef-filled waters, and he would much prefer to bring his vessel into such waters when a good swell is running so that the breakers will help him locate the submerged reefs.

Alignment of breakers. This same process of "feeling bottom" accounts for the fact that waves break parallel to the beach regardless of the direction in which the beach is aligned or the offshore direction from which the waves are approaching. As the shoreward end of a wave reaches the critical depth of about one-half the wave length, it is slowed down. The rest of the wave in deeper water continues on at the deepwater speed until it too comes into shallow water and is slowed down. Thus the adjustment of the wave to the alignment of the shore is somewhat comparable to a row of marching soldiers executing a turn. One end is slowed down, while the rest continue on until they too slow down as they become lined up and the whole row moves forward in the new direction.

It is this dependence of shallow-water waves on the depth of the bottom that makes the waters shoreward of a submarine canyon such excellent anchorages. The longer-period waves tend to be "pulled in" toward the shallower areas on either side of the canyon where much of the wave energy is dissipated; while over the canyon, wave action is considerably less, and the areas shoreward of the canyon head receive considerably less energy. This same phenomenon also accounts for the great concentration of wave energy along prominent headlands as opposed to the quiet pocket beaches that may be between them. It has also been found that aerial photographs of the pattern of wave fronts approaching an unknown coast can be used as a means of producing rough charts of the bottom topography.

A dramatic example of how this wave refraction, as it is called, can affect the works of man was provided when it was discovered that a small hump on the sea floor off Long Beach, California, acted as a lens to focus the wave energy on one particular portion of the Long Beach breakwater. This happened only when the waves came from one particular direction, but in 1930 and again in 1939, storms well offshore generated waves that approached Long Beach from exactly this direction, and in both cases they demolished the one section of the breakwater on which the wave energy was focused.

The seventh wave. A popular myth that somehow is perpetuated by successive generations of novice surfers is that every seventh wave, or every ninth wave, is a big one. It is well known that some waves approaching the shore are bigger than others, and in some cases these big ones may arrive at fairly regular intervals for relatively long periods of time. The mythical nature of the seventh or ninth wave idea becomes obvious when it is realized how these bigger waves are formed. Much of the time, swell—the waves from distant storms—is arriving from two or more different directions as the result of storms in different parts of the ocean. If two or more unrelated wave trains are superimposed one upon the other, a crest of one arriving coincidentally with the trough of another will essentially cancel each other out. By the same token, a crest of one arriving at the same time as a crest of another will result in a reinforced wave that will indeed be higher than those before or after it. For a short time, these higher waves may in fact arrive at fairly regular intervals. But the position and intensity of storms at sea are anything but permanent, and the characteristics of the various wave trains arriving at any given surfing beach are constantly changing. Therefore, any generalizations about the continued regular occurrence of these higher reinforced waves should be viewed with the greatest of skepticism, regardless of how brawny the surfer who advances the information.

Wave damage. The release of energy as waves break can be a terrifying thing. This is especially true when large storm-generated waves crash into a rocky headland or a breakwater built out into deep water. Tillamook Rock Light, situated on a lonely rock off the coast of Oregon, has witnessed some amazing waves. Rocks thrown high by the crashing waves have on several occasions broken the beacon at a height of 140 feet, and a rock weighing 135 pounds was once thrown through the roof of the lightkeeper's house 100 feet above the sea. Breakwaters are especially prone to wave attack. The one at Cherbourg, France, has seen many storms, and during one the waves picked up a rock weighing over two tons and hurled it over the 30-foot-high breakwater, and pieces of the breakwater weighing as much as 65 tons were moved several tens of feet.

The more gently sloping beaches can also come under violent wave attack, as was tragically demonstrated by the highly destructive waves that pounded the east coast of the United States in the winter of 1962. In this case, a high tide and an additional increase in water level brought about by the strong onshore winds, raised sea level sufficiently far that the waves broke not where they normally would, but well inland. There the released energy reduced summer cottages to great piles of jackstraws and wrought havoc with the shore by removing thousands of cubic yards of sand.

Tsunamis. Probably the most terrifying waves, however, are the tsunamis or seismic sea waves, more popularly known as "tidal waves" although the waves have nothing whatsoever to do with the tides. The oceanographers have for years tried to remove the term "tidal wave" from the literature in favor of the Japanese word for "great wave," *tsunami,* but the term is firmly entrenched. For the layman it seems to have a connotation of terror not associated with either of the other more accurate terms.

These relatively rare waves are created by violent disturbances at sea that cause a sudden displacement of a large volume of water. Undersea earthquakes that create a sudden uplifting or down-dropping of a portion of the ocean floor are the most prevalent cause of tsunamis, although a violent volcanic eruption underwater, or possibly a landslide, may also start such a wave. The eruption of Krakatoa off the island of Java in 1883 was accompanied by a tsunami that left over 36,000 dead in its wake and was recorded at tide gauges as far away as England. The great damage and loss of life in the Lisbon earthquake of 1755 was due primarily to the large tsunami that was generated and swept through the city. This wave also raced across the Atlantic, and increasing in height as it entered shallow water, it was recorded in the West Indies at a height of nearly 20 feet.

In more recent times, tsunamis have caused widespread damage in the Hawaiian Islands. At 2 A.M., Hawaiian Time, on the morning of April 1, 1946, a violent earthquake took place deep below the Aleutian Trench south of Unimak Island in the Aleutians. The lighthouse on Scotch Cap on the island, which stood 57 feet above sea level, was destroyed within minutes after the quake by a wave estimated to have been more than 100 feet high. Like the pebble thrown into the pond, the wave radiated out in all directions and, traveling at a speed later calculated as 490 miles an hour, raced across the Pacific to hit the Hawaiian Islands in less than five hours. In some areas of the islands, water rose to a height of more than 50 feet above sea level. When the waves receded, they left behind a death toll of 173 and property damage estimated at $25,000,000.

These really are incredible waves. Their wave height in deep water is probably no greater than two or three feet; their wave length, however, is usually more than 100 miles, and the wave period varies between 15 minutes and one hour. This means that the wave velocity is on the order of several hundred miles per hour. Because of their exceptionally long wave length, these waves essentially "feel bottom" all the time as they cross the ocean, and the shape of the wave front is therefore modified by the submarine topography all along its route. As the wave enters the shallow water along a coast, it is still traveling at these incredible speeds, so the slowing-down process caused by the shoaling water is much more violent than for the normal wind wave. Thus the increase in wave height is greater, and the energy release attendant upon its reaching shallow water is tremendous.

The effect of a tsunami on an exposed coast facing the oncoming wave seems to be most directly related to the underwater topography directly offshore. As with other waves, the greatest concentration of wave energy is shoreward of submarine ridges, and the energy released is considerably less in the lee of submarine valleys. Some of the Hawaiian headlands projecting out into deep water did not provide sufficient shallow water for the 1946 wave to build up, and it was almost unnoticed. Elsewhere, offshore reefs dissipated much of the energy. Some valleys tended to collect and concentrate the energy, although in others this effect was not seen. A good deal of research still needs to be done to determine the various factors that influence the effect of tsunamis as they approach and inundate the shore.

A singularly ingenious technique has been developed by the U.S. Coast and Geodetic Survey for predicting the arrival times of tsunamis at distant points in the Pacific. This Seismic Sea Wave Warning System, as it is called, has been credited with saving many lives subsequent to the 1946 wave at Hawaii that resulted in its establishment. When an earthquake occurs, its position is quickly pinpointed by the seismograph stations operated by the Coast and Geodetic Survey and by several cooperating countries. If the epicenter—the point on the surface of the earth directly above the point of disturbance—lies in the ocean, then the nearby tide-gauge stations are alerted to watch for any evidence of a tsunami. Many of these stations are now equipped with a "tsunami recorder" hooked to an automatic alarm system to alert a nearby installation of the presence of such a wave. The gauge is checked, and the moment of the arrival of the first wave is quickly radioed to a central message center at Honolulu. Knowing the time of origin, the estimated time of arrival at Hawaii can be determined by reference to a previously constructed travel-time chart centered upon the Hawaiian Islands.

This travel-time chart, shown in Figure 3, shows the location of the various tide stations and the seismograph stations in the Coast and Geodetic Survey's Seismic Sea Wave Warning System. It also shows the travel time to Honolulu, Hawaii, for a tsunami generated anywhere in the Pacific. From this chart, it can be seen that it would

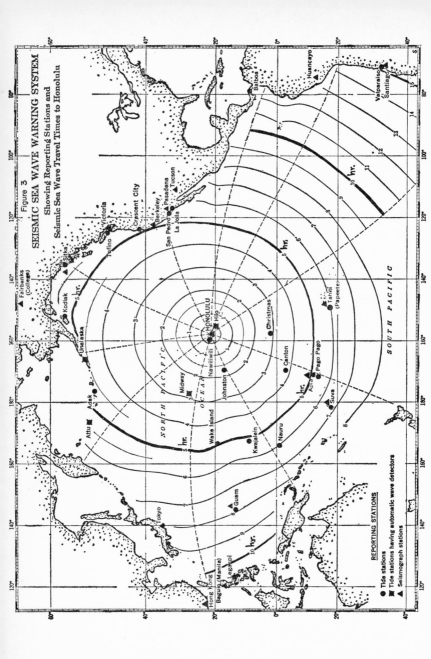

Figure 3

SEISMIC SEA WAVE WARNING SYSTEM

Showing Reporting Stations and
Seismic Sea Wave Travel Times to Honolulu

REPORTING STATIONS

● Tide stations
◼ Tide stations having automatic wave detectors
▲ Seismograph stations

48

take between 4½ and 5 hours for a wave generated in the Aleutian Trench to travel to Hawaii, and about 15 hours for one generated near the coast of Chile. Once the predicted time of arrival has been determined, this information is flashed to the civilian authorities so that the populace can be evacuated from potentially dangerous areas. At present, only the time of arrival of the wave can be predicted, but we hope that research now in progress will eventually enable the Coast and Geodetic Survey also to provide data on the anticipated height of the onrushing wave. These waves of destructive proportions are not a common occurrence, but the tremendous loss of life and costly property damage when they do hit more than justifies the relatively small outlay for an effective warning system.

Major destructive tsunamis are more common in the Pacific than in the other arms of the global sea. Tsunamis in the Atlantic (primarily in the Puerto Rico area) have been small ones, except for the 1755 Lisbon wave. Nevertheless, if there was one exception, there could be two. The possible consequences of a full-scale tsunami crashing unheralded into the Atlantic coast of North America on a warm Sunday afternoon in midsummer are horrible to contemplate. The chances of this happening, however, are slight—hardly sufficient reason to cancel those vacation plans for Nantucket in favor of a trip to the Canadian Rockies.

TIDES

Although "tidal wave" is frowned on as a term for tsunamis, the term is a legitimate one when referring to the tide. The rise and fall of the tide along the shore is actually the coastal manifestation of a long-period wave. The tide wave along most coasts has a period of about 12½ hours. This is the most noticeable wave caused by the tidal forces, although there are many others with much smaller heights whose periods range up to as much as 19 years. The longest known waves in the ocean are those associated with the tide-producing forces, and the wave form is readily apparent on the records of the more than one hundred tide gauges maintained along the coasts of the United States by the U.S. Coast and Geodetic Survey.

These records are in many respects very similar to the records that might be made by a single train of regular wind waves, except that instead of periods of a few seconds, these waves have periods of many hours. A typical tide curve is shown in Figure 4. Because of their importance in commerce and coastal engineering, the tides have received a lot of attention since Pytheas in the fourth century B.C. first ascribed the rise and fall of the waters along the shores of the English Channel to the influence of the moon.

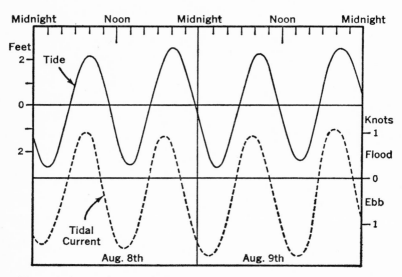

Figure 4. Curves showing the variation in tidal height and in tidal current velocity over a two-day period at The Narrows in New York Harbor.

Causes of tides. The tide-producing forces are directly related to the combined attractive forces of the sun and the moon on the rotating earth, and the attractive forces depend both on the size of these bodies and on their distance from the earth. Although the sun is much larger than the moon, it is at such a great distance away that its tide-producing power is somewhat less than half that of the moon. The attraction of the sun and moon for the solid earth as a whole is considered as being concentrated at the center of the earth—its center of mass. Yet the waters of the ocean are only a relatively thin film lying some 4,000 miles above this center of mass. Thus the attraction of the sun and moon for this surface film is different from that for the solid earth as a whole, and these differences of attraction give rise to the forces that cause the waters of the global sea to move relative to the solid earth. It is these motions that are called the *tide*.

The regular variations in the astronomical tides are thus related to the variations in the positions of the sun and moon relative to the earth. At times of new and full moon, for example, the sun and the moon are "pulling" in the same direction, and the tide has a greater range—that is, high tides are higher and low tides are lower. These are the *spring tides* that occur twice each month. The *neap tides,* which also occur twice monthly, are the lowest ranges, which occur midway between new and full moon and between full and the next new moon. At these times the attractive forces of the sun and moon are at right angles to each other and tend to cancel out rather than to reinforce each other. This relationship is shown in Figure 5.

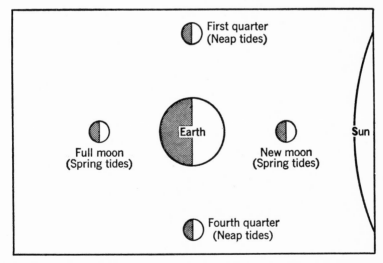

Figure 5. Schematic representation of the positions of the sun and moon relative to the earth at four stages in the monthly tidal cycle. When the attractive forces of the sun and moon are in line, the monthly highs or spring tides are produced. When the forces are at right angles, the monthly lows or neap tides result.

In addition to these tidal variations related to the moon's *phase,* there is the annual variation in the earth's distance from the sun and the monthly variation in its distance from the moon, the so-called *parallax* effects. The *declination* of the moon (its distance north or south of the plane of the equator) also affects the tide by varying the relative heights of the two tides per day.

People often ask why there are in many places two high tides per day when the moon passes overhead only once a day. What happens is that the moon causes two tidal bulges on the earth at the same time. One is on the portion of the earth's surface which is directly under the moon, the other is on the exact opposite side of the earth. In simplest terms, the explanation for these two bulges is that the moon attracts the water away from the earth on the side nearer the moon; but on the opposite side of the earth, the attractive force on the water is less than it is on the solid earth whose center is some 4,000 miles closer to the moon. The earth is, in effect, pulled away from the water on this side to form the second tidal bulge. Thus, as the earth turns, making one complete revolution each day, every point on the surface is subjected once to each of these two bulges, making two high tides per day. It is the inequality of these two daily high tides at any one place that is caused by the moon's distance north or south of the equator. There are other variables, but those related to phase, parallax, and declination are the three major ones.

The tide-producing forces are distributed evenly over the earth, varying with the latitude. But the response of the various arms of the ocean to these forces differs from place to place, depending upon the shape of the ocean bottom and the configuration of the interfering land masses. Thus the actual tides encountered at different places on the earth vary markedly. They range from the relatively small tides in the Mediterranean Sea and the Gulf of Mexico to the extreme tides of the Bay of Fundy, where spring tide ranges of up to 50 feet have been measured.

Other sea level variations. Factors other than the sun and moon affect the level of the sea. Winds can cause an increase or a decrease in sea level as they pile up water against the shore or move it out.

Changes in the atmospheric pressure cause changes in sea level, for the surface of the sea rises in response to a drop in atmospheric pressure that oceanographers refer to as the inverted barometer effect. A given mass of warm water will stand higher than the same mass of cold water, so even water temperature has an effect on sea level. In harbors, the effect of river discharge may be significant. At Philadelphia, for example, the tide-gauge records have shown over the years that the astronomical tides are often completely masked by variations in the volume of flow of the Delaware River. In lower New York Harbor, on the other hand, changes in the harbor level attributable to changes in the flow of the Hudson River are almost imperceptible, but onshore winds will move large quantities of water into the harbor, where their presence is easily detected on the tide records.

The maintenance of accurate tide records along the coasts of the world is of great importance to the engineer. Not only are the data from these records of use in determining the height to which coastal structures must be built to be safely above the level of water damage, but it is by these records that a value for mean sea level is determined. *Mean sea level* is the plane from which elevations on land are measured, and it is defined as the plane about which the tide oscillates.

Accurate records maintained for many years by the Coast and Geodetic Survey have shown that sea level on the east coast of the United States has been rising at an average rate of just over one foot in a hundred years, while on the west coast the rate has been just half that. Since the global sea is one sea, it might be expected that the rate of rise would be the same on both coasts, and most probably in actuality it is. But the tide gauges can measure the water level only in relation to the land on which they are situated. Thus on the Pacific coast, the sea-level data suggest that a rise in land level has in part masked the rise of sea level. This is indeed quite possible, as the west coast of North America is bordered by relatively young mountain ranges where such upward growth is still to be expected.

In southeast Alaska, on the other hand, the land has been rising in one area at such a rapid rate that sea level actually appears to have fallen within the past 60 years. This situation was investigated by the Coast and Geodetic Survey by reoccupying all stations in the Juneau area where tide gauges had previously been installed and relating the new sea-level data to that derived from the gauge at Juneau that has been in continuous operation for many years. In this way, it was discovered that the land had been rising over a fairly large area, with the maximum uplift of about five feet occurring in the area of Haines, Alaska.

This regional uplift may be a response to mountain-building forces deep within the earth, or it may be a slow recovery from the weight of the ice that covered the area during the Pleistocene ice ages. Such slow rebound from a thick ice cover has been measured for years in the northern Great Lakes area and in the Scandinavian peninsula. Regardless of the reason, the fact that the stated elevations of known points on land were no longer accurate caused no end of confusion and consternation to the engineers and mappers working in this part of Alaska. Throughout the whole ocean, however, sea level is probably rising slowly as the polar ice caps gradually melt and add their water to the sea.

The daily, monthly, and annual variations in sea level as well as the longer-period variations and the irregular variations also provide the oceanographer with a valuable tool for keeping track of what is going on in the ocean. They provide the marine researcher with an invaluable past history of the patient. For example, when the west coast of North America in the winter of 1957-1958 suddenly experienced an unseasonal warming of the coastal waters that was a boon to the tuna fishermen but spelled disaster for the northern salmon industry, the warming was accompanied by a rise in sea level. When oceanographers from all over the country met at Rancho Santa Fe, in California, with all the available information that bore on this strange behavior of the ocean, tide records extending back into the last century were the only long series of marine data that could be brought to bear on the problem. This anomalously warm water appears to be related to a shift in the wind pattern, which in turn changed the pattern of movement of the coastal waters, bringing in warm water where cold water had previously been. By the tidal records, the passage of storms up the coast can also be traced, and oceanographers at the University of Miami have discovered that variations in the speed of the Florida Current portion of the Gulf Stream can be monitored by noting the difference in variations in sea level at Miami and at the Cat Cay gauge across the strait in the Bahamas.

TIDAL CURRENTS

The rise and fall of the tide is everywhere accompanied by a horizontal motion of the water, the tidal currents. These are especially important to the movement of shipping in our crowded harbors. They were particularly critical during the days of sail. When the captain said "We sail with the tide," he was referring not to the vertical motion of the tide, but to the tidal currents. In a place like the Narrows between Staten Island and Long Island at the entrance to New York Harbor, it was usually necessary for sailing ships to move in with the flood tide and out with the ebb tide. Even today in the East River around Hell Gate, the tugs with their long strings of barges usually await the turn of the tide before they attempt the narrow passage with its strong currents.

Tidal currents together with the vertical movement of the tide are part of the same phenomenon caused by the tide-producing forces of the sun and moon (see Figure 4). They are, therefore, periodic and, like the tides, may be predicted well in advance. It is in their periodic nature that the tidal currents are different from all other currents in the sea.

Reversing tidal currents. In harbors, estuaries, and in narrow, constricted passages, the most familiar form of tidal movement is the reversing tidal current. Ideally, the cycle begins with *flood current* flowing into the harbor and reaching a maximum velocity called *strength of flood* at about mid-flood. Then the velocity decreases to zero, called *slack water* or *slack before ebb*. The *ebb* or

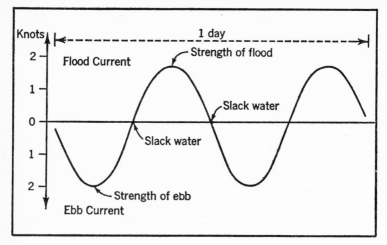

Figure 6. Tidal-current curve showing the typical reversal of flow and illustrating the terms used in describing reversing tidal currents.

outflowing tide then begins, builds up to *strength of ebb,* and then decreases to *slack before flood,* and the cycle repeats itself. (See Figure 6.) As would be expected, maximum velocities at strength of flood and ebb are encountered at times of spring tides, whereas lower values occur during neap tides.

Similarly, non-astronomic factors, such as wind set-up and river run-off, also affect the movement of reversing tidal currents. In New York Harbor the outflow from the Hudson River has a significant effect on the reversing tidal currents. As might be expected, it not only increases the velocity at strength of ebb and decreases it at strength of flood, but it also results in a longer duration of the ebb current than the flood.

There is an interesting phenomenon connected with the tidal currents in New York Harbor and the Hudson River that has been discovered there only within the past several years. From extensive measurements of the currents both at the surface and at depth, it was found that the outflow of the Hudson River increases the duration and strength of the ebb currents only part way down to the bottom. This is reasonable, when it is realized that the river water is fresh and would tend to override the denser salt water. At mid-depths, the inflowing and outflowing currents were about the same. However, near the bottom, it was found that both the strength and the duration of the inflowing flood currents were considerably more than the ebb. In other words, in addition to the back-and-forth tidal motion, there appeared to be more water coming into the harbor along the bottom than was going out at these depths. This anomaly was investigated at profiles of current stations all the way up the river as far as West Point, and the same thing was found. There was a net transport of water up the harbor along the bottom. Because the surface water became more and more saline as it moved down the river and through the harbor, it obviously was being mixed with the underlying salt water and carrying great quantities of salt water out with it. To make up for this salt water lost by mixing, a return flow was moving into the harbor from seaward along the bottom.

Comparable up-harbor bottom flow was already known from the lower Chesapeake Bay, where it is an important mechanism because it moves upstream the small forms of fish and shellfish that then mature in the upper bay. In New York Harbor, however, up-harbor bottom currents had not been found before, and their importance to problems of silt accumulation, waste disposal, and possible contamination from any offshore release of radioactive material was quite obvious.

Rotary tidal currents. Tidal currents are reversing currents only when they are confined to a narrow passage. In the open ocean, tidal currents are rotary in nature—that is, they change direction in a regular manner, with the direction of flow changing through a full circle approximately every 12 hours. Rotary tidal currents have been measured at many places in the sea and have been detected at depths of over a mile. They are usually found superimposed upon some non-tidal current. Thus the velocity and direction of the non-tidal flow is usually modified by these rotary tidal currents, perhaps to the extent that the flow has a pattern of a whole series of loops.

OTHER OCEAN CURRENTS

It is the non-tidal currents, however, that constitute the major circulation pattern of the global sea. Some of the ocean currents are transient things, but the major surface currents flow in relatively well-defined general patterns. The Gulf Stream, first described by Ponce de León in 1513, is probably the most celebrated of the permanent currents. Thought for a long time to be a narrow, fast-moving ribbon of water, a "river in the sea," this most famous of the ocean currents has recently been shown to be instead a rather complex system of separate filaments whose motions are anything but regular. The eddies that break off and dissipate and the constantly changing location, speed, and direction of the various strands make the whole system more comparable to the streams and curls of smoke rising from a cigarette. This is the day-to-day "weather" within the current, but on a broad global scale, the geographer is more interested in the overall "climate," the average positions and directions of the major permanent surface currents.

World current pattern. Around the great Antarctic continent is a broad, sluggish current moving predominantly from west to east, called the West Wind Drift. In the three major arms of the sea, the patterns of the surface currents are really very similar, the pattern in each being divided into two main portions, one north and one south of the equator. The northern parts of the Atlantic and Pacific each contain a large clockwise circulation pattern in which the north-flowing current along the west side is narrower and faster than the broad, slow-moving southerly return current on the eastern side of the circular pattern, or gyre, as it is called. In the North Atlantic, of course, this strong western side of the gyre is the Gulf Stream. Its Pacific counterpart is the very similar but less spectacular Japan Current, or Kuroshio, meaning "black stream," so named because of the darker color of its water. In both the Atlantic and the Pacific, a cooler current swings down from the northern polar regions to join this circular pattern in the northwest. In the Atlantic this is the Laborador Current; its Pacific twin is the

Oyashio, and both bring ice down from the colder regions farther north.

The northern part of the Indian Ocean is different from the other two major arms of the global sea, for it is relatively small north of the Equator and is completely sealed off to the north by the land mass of southern Asia, which restricts the full development of a comparable gyre. Rather there are small clockwise gyres on either side of the Indian Peninsula.

The equatorial circulation in the Atlantic, Pacific, and Indian oceans is very similar. In each basin there are two major westward-flowing currents, the North and the South Equatorial Current, and between them in each case flows a narrow eastward-moving Equatorial Countercurrent. The similarity of the patterns is so strong that when in 1952 a new current flowing below the surface was discovered in the Equatorial Pacific, oceanographers were so sure that a comparable current would be found in the Equatorial Atlantic that no special expedition was sent out specifically to look for it. Rather they waited until one of the ships from the Woods Hole Oceanographic Institution happened to be crossing this area and had the time to stop exactly where they felt the current should be and "discover" it. It was indeed there.

Even though the Indian Ocean exhibits the typical three-current equatorial circulation pattern at the surface, there is some doubt as to whether this branch of the global sea is sufficiently similar to the other two to have this same undercurrent. One of the many aims of the International Indian Ocean Expedition now under way is to investigate the possibility that such a current also exists there. Another interesting aspect of the Indian Ocean now being investigated is the seasonal shift in the surface current direction in response to the seasonal change in wind direction. During part of the year, the Northeast Monsoon winds move the surface waters to the west. Then these winds die down, to be replaced by the Southwest Monsoons, which eventually get the surface waters moving in the opposite direction.

In this mechanism, the Indian Ocean presents the oceanographer with a unique opportunity to study the relationship of surface winds to surface currents. How long, for example, does it take a wind of what velocity to blow over how long a stretch of ocean before a surface current is generated, and what is the direction and speed of this current relative to the wind that causes it? The Indian Ocean makes the ideal laboratory to study such a problem.

In the southern parts of the Atlantic, Pacific, and Indian oceans, the circulation patterns of the surface waters are again very similar to one another and essentially mirror images of their northern counterparts. The westward-flowing South Equatorial Current in each case contributes part of its waters to the western portion of a large counterclockwise gyre, as opposed to the clockwise circulation in the northern hemisphere. Flowing southward, these waters contribute to the West Wind Drift around Antarctica that forms the southern quarter of the circular pattern. This eastward movement then contributes to the north-flowing currents along the west coast of South America (the Peru, or Humbolt, Current), Africa (the Benguela Current), and Australia (the West Australian Current). Each of these northerly currents then joins its respective equatorial circulation moving westward, and the gyre is complete.

Causes of global currents. Our knowledge of the causes of the surface circulation in the ocean is far from complete, but the atmospheric wind circulation as it affects the waters on a rotating earth is the major contributing factor. The prevailing westerlies overlie the general areas occupied by the slow currents moving from west to east at the high-latitude sides of the current gyres of both the northern and southern hemispheres. The West Wind Drift around Antarctica, for example, underlies the strong west winds that gave this region the nickname "the roaring forties." The major portions of the circular current gyres underlie the subtropical anticyclonic winds, whereas the equatorial current pattern is a fairly good watery reproduction of the pattern of the overlying trade winds with the narrow band of the doldrums in between.

Even though the patterns are indeed similar, the exact mechanism whereby the winds induce motion in the water is anything but clear. The mechanism is obviously a highly complex one. Not only have we learned that the wind can, by friction, move a surface layer of water without even creating a ripple, but it also appears that the part of the surface that has the most marked response to the wind is not the large waves, but the very small ripples and apparently minor "bumps" in the sea surface. If we will admit that the atmospheric circulation is the major cause for the observed general pattern of surface circulation in the ocean, then the western intensification of the currents along the western boundaries of the northern ocean to produce the Gulf Stream and the Kuroshio can be explained by the added element of the earth's rotation. Since the earth turns from the west toward the east, this rotation introduces an additional force that tends to displace the centers of circulation to the west, causing compression of the western part of the current pattern and intensification of the currents flowing along the western sides of the ocean.

Factors other than just the wind also have an influence on the large-scale movement of the ocean waters. The most important of these factors are the differences in density of the waters in various parts of the ocean. Cool water is denser than warm water, and waters of higher salt content are denser than those of lower salinity. Thus waters of relatively high density can be formed by cooling or by increasing the salinity, as by evaporation or by the formation of ice. Wherever the density of the water exceeds that of the water immediately below it, it will sink until it encounters water of the same density. It then spreads out. It is probably by this mechanism operating in the high latitudes that waters of the deep sea are gradually renewed. Other factors such as water depth, underwater topography, and the location of land barriers also have an effect on the over-all circulation pattern of the ocean.

Rip currents. To return briefly from this quick look at the global picture to a smaller-scale current with a more direct personal implication, the rip currents along many of the world's better bathing beaches have needlessly claimed the lives of many a good swimmer. These lives could have been saved had the swimmers but known what they were dealing with. It is easy to understand why a swimmer would panic when he suddenly feels himself being carried out to sea. He naturally turns back and increases his stroke only to find that he is still losing ground to a current that may be moving seaward as fast as two miles an hour. He rapidly tires and then panics, as his frantic cries for help are unheard above the pounding of the surf.

Rarely are these rip currents as wide as 100 feet, and they always die out in an eddy not far seaward of the surf zone. The swimmer who recognizes that he is being carried out to sea by such a current can do one of two things to get back. He can turn and swim parallel to the shore and soon be out of the current, or he can relax and be carried out to the point where the current becomes a slow eddy and then swim back casually along a different route.

Along the beaches of southern California, surfers often utilize these rip currents to get back out where the big ones are peaking up. It is much easier to be carried out sitting casually on your board than to have to paddle your way out through the surf.

A rip current can usually be spotted from the shore by a foam line or a line of agitated or confused water that runs straight out from the beach. Where the current goes through the surf zone, there is usually a pronounced interruption in the long line of breakers. These currents are the means whereby water that accumulates along the shore is returned seaward, and they are most common when the waves out in deep water are approaching the coast parallel to the shoreline. When the waves approach at an angle to the coast, there usually develops along the shore a current that moves steadily in the general direction in which the waves are moving before they "feel bottom" and swing in parallel to the beach. Such longshore currents usually prevent the formation of rips along a straight beach, but may themselves become rips where the longshore current is deflected seaward by a breakwater or rocky headland. If every swimmer were familiar with rip currents and how to avoid or get out of them, summertime would be far less tragic for many families.

The motion in the ocean seems to hold a special charm for

mathematicians, and they are constantly devising and revising their mathematical models in an attempt to explain singularly complex interrelationships that result in the movement of ocean water. It is one of the few aspects of the study of the sea that lends itself to mathematical treatments. When there are enough capable mathematicians and physicists working on the great array of problems that are presented by the moving waters of the global sea, perhaps then we will have more of the answers to the questions with which we are now faced. On the other hand, the history of oceanographic research has shown that for every question answered, the study presents more new questions that demand to be answered. Thus the study of the sea goes on.

In the first half of the nineteenth century, the great naturalist Edward Forbes declared, as the result of his studies of marine life in the eastern Mediterranean, that there was no life in the ocean below a depth of 300 fathoms (1,800 feet). Below this depth, he claimed, was the "Azoic Zone"—the lifeless zone. There then followed the great age of biological dredging during which every biologist who could talk his way aboard a ship took a bottom dredge along with him and proceeded to disprove the existence of the "Azoic Zone."

Actually, Forbes was a magnificent marine biologist, and his was the first attempt to make a systematic study of the geographical distribution of marine organisms on a world-wide scale. His postulation of "Azoic Zone" was probably a justifiable conclusion from his work in the Mediterranean; but even though the extension of the idea to a global scale was wrong, the mere postulation of the existence of a zone of no life provided a great impetus to the study of life in the deep sea. By the time he had been well disproved, there had been so much work done on the fauna of the deep sea that the subject itself was sufficiently fascinating to engage and hold the attention of marine biologists.

THE ABUNDANCE

Even though there are some "deserts" in the sea where little life is found, these are the exceptions. The greatest part of the global sea is literally teeming with life. In places the surface of a calm sea may suddenly be churned into a froth as a large school of small fish breaks the surface in their frantic attempt to escape some predator beneath. In other places a broad brown blanket made up of countless millions of microscopic organisms may extend as far as the eye can see.

Beneath the surface of the sea, the diver who swims through the channels and passages of a coral reef and drifts above its colorful shapes cannot fail to be impressed by the abundance and incredible variety of life all around him. An amazing phenomenon to witness underwater is the wheeling and turning of a large school of fish as though they were parading on some great three-dimensional parade ground. As they move away from you, they appear as a transparent screen; but then, as though in response to a drillmaster's command, they all turn at precisely the same instant to present a brilliant flash of silver as they make a solid wall of moving life. Often these course changes come at regular intervals, and you seem to be watching a great flashing signal light as the school moves off into the distance.

When an oceanographic ship stops at night to lower bottles for water samples or to obtain a core of the bottom sediments, a bright light is usually placed at the rail to attract life from the upper layers. Even though there have been few signs of life during the day, almost always the brilliant spot beneath the light is soon swarming with moving animals. Small squid are common; by taking water in through one tube and ejecting it rapidly through another, they effectively jet themselves into the patch of light.

THE VARIATIONS

Life in the sea is indeed abundant, but it is also tremendously varied, and it is with these variations that the marine biologist is primarily concerned. The variations in the geographical distribution of life, in the adaptation of life within the marine environment, and in the form and habits of the life within the sea also hold great interest for the less scientifically oriented observer of the global sea.

Deep life. The possibility of some especially strange variety of life in the very deepest parts of the sea has led men to probe ever deeper with their biological dredges and their various types of diving bells. Certainly a region of constant cold temperature and enormous pressures must, if it sustains life at all, harbor some very strange creatures. The pressure at these depths is tremendous. The pressure of the overlying water increases at the rate of about four pounds per square inch for every nine feet of depth. Thus at a depth of 30,000 feet in a deep-sea trench, the pressures are nearly seven tons per square inch, as opposed to the approximately 15 pounds per square inch to which man is subjected at sea level.

The animals of the deepest sea thus must withstand pressures about a thousand times greater than those at surface. Yet the dredgings of the Soviet ship *Vityaz* in the Kurile-Kamchatka Trench, the Swedish *Albatross* in the Puerto Rico Trench, and the Danish *Galathea* in the Mindanao Deep of the Philippine Trench all recovered life from these great depths. In the Mindanao Deep, for example, the *Galathea* recovered a sea anemone, a whitish creature brought up still attached to the stone on which he had rested some six miles below the surface. At first it appeared quite comparable to the more familiar forms known from shallow water. But on closer examination, it was so different that it did not fit into any known family of sea anemones, and a new one had to be created for this one specimen. Also recovered from this trench were sea cucumbers, mollusks, small shrimp-like organisms, worms, and bacteria. With the discovery of bacteria at these depths, there remained no environment on earth where these tiny forms have not been found. It had for years been thought that fish—that is, fish with backbones—are not found at these great depths. However, the two men aboard the U.S. Navy's bathyscaph *Trieste* in its deepest dive in the Mariannas Trench actually saw a fish at a depth of 35,800 feet.

So no depth in the sea is devoid of fish, but many of those in the deeper parts of the ocean have evolved into strange forms. Sunlight penetrates only about a thousand feet into the sea, so at greater depths the fish have developed over the centuries strange variations in their means of capturing food. Some have mouths several times larger than their bodies; others have developed luminous organs inside their mouths that lure their prey into these gaping maws. One of the so-called angler fish has a pole-like appendage from its head that extends out before it, bearing at the end a small light organ that is actually armed with hooks. This amazing fish is only about three inches long, but travels under the burdensome name of *Lasiognathus saccostoma.*

The problem of finding a mate in these dark waters has been neatly solved by one of these angler fishes. The female of the species travels about with one or more dwarfed males permanently attached to her as parasites. She thus assures that her eggs will be fertilized when they are ready and obviates the problem of having to locate a male at this critical time.

Living fossils. As is true of so many aspects of oceanography, there are also two schools of thought on the antiquity of the deep-sea fauna. One side maintains that the lack of environmental variation in the deep sea—that is, the relatively unchanging condition of darkness, cold, great pressure, and geographical isolation—has affectively prevented the organic evolution normally brought about by adaptation to varying environmental conditions. Thus they expect that the deep sea would contain primitive forms that are the "living fossil" ancestors of the more specialized life found elsewhere in the sea. The opposing school of thought says that the deep sea, like any other extreme environment, has certain forms that have migrated there from elsewhere, survived the rigors of the region, and multiplied to become the dominant elements of this restricted and specialized fauna. They would, therefore, not be the oldest forms, but rather a more recent colonizer from some other environment. This scholarly argument is still being waged between Soviet and American scientists in one of the most heated but friendly of international controversies.

Regardless of the degree of antiquity of these deep animals, it is true that there are some very old and primitive forms of life that have apparently managed to survive without evolution and change. Today they are regarded as "living fossils" that somehow kept in a backwash of the evolutionary stream. One such form was a small one-shelled mollusk brought to the surface by the *Galathea* expedition. In appearance it resembled a one-shelled clam or perhaps a limpet, but such a shellfish had never before been recovered from the sea. It developed that its shell and internal structure were the same as those of a mollusk called *Pilina* which had been extinct for some 350,000,000 years and was known only as a fossil. The new form was so radically different from present-day mollusks that a special class was created for this one species, and it was named *Neopilina galatheae* in honor of both its close but ancient relative and the ship that first dredged it from the bottom of the sea.

For many years, biologists have believed that the fishes of the sea somehow developed appendages that were less fin-like and more leg-like prior to the time that the first amphibian emerged from the sea to invade the land at the end of the Devonian period some 300,000,-000 years ago. This anatomical link between the fishes and the amphibians was one of the classic "missing links."

Then in 1938 off the east coast of Africa, a fisherman came up with a fish that was totally unknown to him. It eventually came to the attention of a zoologist who identified it as an authentic coelacanth, an ancient form of fish thought to have become extinct some 70,000,000 years ago. This fish was one of the great group of very primitive fish with the staggering name of crossopterygians. These were the link between the fish and the amphibians, and here was a chance for man to study at first hand the interesting anatomy of a true "missing link." Since then, at least ten more specimens of this fish have been recovered, and its anatomy has been thoroughly studied. The coelacanth is a good-sized fish: the adult may weigh nearly 200 pounds and be over five feet in length. The coelacanth's fins, instead of being attached to the main body directly, are on a scaly stalk protruding from the body—much more similar to the present mammalian appendages than is the ordinary fin. It is intriguing that these creatures have not changed organically since their ancestors roamed the Silurian and Devonian seas many millions of years ago. Without a doubt, these are the oldest "higher animals" on our earth.

Amazing migrations. The migrations of marine organisms are still as mystifying as are those of the birds and the lemmings. The

American and European eels, for example, mingle in their early stages in the general area of the Sargasso Sea, the center of the North Atlantic gyre. Yet the two species unerringly sort themselves out on their great migrations north, the American species heading back to the rivers on the North American Continent while the European species somehow reach the rivers of western Europe. Actually, no one knew where these eels came from until just a few years ago. The young ones would suddenly appear each year seaward of the mouths of the rivers and start upstream without having been spotted anywhere at sea on their way to the rivers. In many biological tows, however, marine biologists had been recovering a singularly non-eel looking specimen to which they had given the name *leptocephalus*. This, it was finally discovered, was the larval stage of the eel, and it is in this form that the great migrations are made. Amazingly enough, the change from *leptocephalus* to the young eel comes at precisely the time they arrive off the mouths of their rivers—about one year for the American forms and three for the European forms, whose trip takes just three times as long.

The Chinook salmon of northwestern North America is another example of marine migration. It is born in a stream, swims downstream as a very small fish, and then may spend as much as five years in the Pacific Ocean at distances of a thousand miles from his birthplace. However, when the time comes to spawn, it unerringly returns to the very same stream from which it started. Some research work recently done on these Chinook salmon suggests that the fish is able to distinguish one stream from another by its characteristic odor, but the problem still is far from solved. This particular problem of the salmon, however, is of considerable economic importance, as it relates to the need for building expensive salmon ladders to get the migrating fish around hydroelectric dams.

The gray whale is another marine organism that undertakes staggeringly long migrations. In the summer, the gray whales feed in the area of the western Bering Sea off the Siberian coast, but each fall they leave for the 12,000-mile trip to a few tiny coastal lagoons along the coast of Baja California, Mexico. There those females who bred the year before give birth to their calves, and the others mate to add to the population the next year.

Scammons Lagoon is one of the few places where these orgies of birth and procreation take place. It is an almost unbelievable thing to witness and can be tremendously exciting in only a small skiff with an outboard. As whales go, the California gray is a medium-sized whale—about 40 feet long—but when one rises from the water right beside you so close that you can smell the fetid odor of his breath as he showers you with water and then dives, lifting his fluked tail high in the air to make a wave that almost swamps your skiff, your respect for the old-time whalers in their small boats rises to new proportions.

The newborn calves are 12 to 14 feet in length, but they leave the lagoons with their parents in the spring for the long trip back to their Arctic feeding grounds. The gray whale population dropped from about 25,000 in 1840 to an estimated total of only 100 animals about 20 years ago. By 1955, however, thanks to their being protected by law, careful counts as they passed close along the California coast and later counts in their lagoons showed the herd then to number about 3,000. Why do they migrate 12,000 miles between their feeding and breeding grounds, when there is an ample food supply near the lagoons and many a good lagoon along the coast of the Bering Sea? We just do not know, but in the process of trying to find out, we are finding out many other things about the sea and its life.

Cleaning stations. "Serendipity" is one of those words whose meaning is so restricted that the occasion to use it seldom presents itself. Yet in the study of the global sea, to find something other than the particular thing for which you were looking is a common occurrence. Here is one example: While carrying out a very detailed study of one particular species of small fish, one of the biologists of the Scripps Institution of Oceanography decided that there were too many problems involved in bringing the fish into the laboratory to study. He therefore donned an aqualung and went down to study the fish in its natural habitat. While observing the fish's habits, he found that the same fish returned regularly to a small patch of rocks, where it would rest motionless for some time. On closer examination, he discovered that a tiny shrimp-like creature rose up from the rocks and began eating the small parasites that infested the gills of the fish. In and out of the gill slits the little cleaner would dart, and the larger fish merely stood there until the cleaning was finished, and then swam off. This discovery obviously was of greater interest to the biologist than the proposed study, and it started a continuing investigation into this "cleaning station" phenomenon. Since then other examples have been found where one fish is "cleaned off" at these underwater "delousing stations" while others patiently await their turns. Often serendipity is a singularly effective agent in advancing our knowledge of the sea.

Struggle for survival. But all is not sweetness and light in the sea, for there is a terrific competition for existence. The food chain, as it is called, starts with the dissolved nutrients that nurture the smallest forms of life in the ocean. These are then eaten by small creatures such as the very abundant copepods—small crustaceans—and they in turn provide food for the larger species, and so on. There are, however, interesting bypasses in the food chain, such as the great blue whale. This mammal weighs as much as 294,000 pounds and grows to 100 feet in length, yet its main food is the microscopic plant and animal life that it filters from the water with the frayed ends of its baleen plates. Then too the food chain is apparently reversed when the smaller forms attack creatures several times their size. Some of the deep-sea forms with distendable stomachs and disjointable jaws can swallow fish several times their own size. Sharks have been known to attack wounded whales, and the killer whale has been observed driving the California gray whales into the beach during their long migrations.

Normally, this killing in the sea is for food, and without it the sea might become a thick slurry of living protoplasm, but the apparently senseless killing that is sometimes observed seems as pointless as man's mass slaughter of many of the species on his lands. The killer whale, for example, apparently kills for the sheer joy of it. To watch a pair of killer whales attack a group of fun-loving sea lions will literally bring tears of impotent rage to your eyes. The sea lions have sensed the danger and have collected into a tight knot with only their necks out of the water as they swivel their heads to keep those two big black square-topped fins in sight. The killers circle the group at a distance, and then turn and race at amazing speed directly for them, cutting through the sea lions as a sharp knife cuts through a piece of tender beef. The screaming of sea lions is almost exactly like that of small children in terrible pain. The water starts to turn crimson, and the killer whales turn back for another run. This time they come more slowly. Rather than slice through the regrouped sea lions this time, they slowly enter the pack, ripping and tearing as they go until the water is a frothing mass of foam and blood and the air is filled with the agonizing cries of the maimed and dying. Then they leave. They do not stop to eat the fruits of their brief labors; they just leave. There is little that you can do from a boat, but your heart aches for the sea lions.

DRIFTING LIFE

The plankton of the global sea—the drifting animals and plants, as opposed to the free-swimmers and those attached to the bottom—constitute without a doubt a greater volume of living material than all the other organisms of the earth put together, including all the trees and animals of the land. Although this sounds like a staggering amount of life, the immensity can be appreciated perhaps when you realize that the animal portion of the plankton—the zooplankton—is found from the surface to the bottom, an average depth range of more than two miles, over nearly three-quarters of the earth's surface. Then add to this the drifting plants—the phytoplankton—that extend from the sea surface down to the lower limit of light penetration sufficient for them to utilize it, or about 200 to 300 feet. When all of this is compared to the relatively thin layer over the land surface that supports the life on the continents, the original statement becomes a bit more credible. But what is this great volume of drifting life composed of, and what does it look like?

If you were to tow a fine-mesh net through the ocean waters almost anywhere, haul it in, and then place whatever you had caught immediately under a microscope, you would see what to oceanographers who have done this many times is still one of the truly amazing sights on this earth. Before you, magnified many times, is a seething, wiggling, darting, twitching mass of the most varied and exotically shaped forms of life you have ever seen. There will be the arrow worms that look like the barbed heads of long spears; the beautiful radiolarians that look like the most ornate of chandeliers; the foraminifera that are the tiniest perfect shells you ever saw; small blobs of life with a long whip with which they lash their way along; others with a crown of short hairs that they wave in unison to propel themselves slowly through the water; the tiniest of shrimp-like animals; some that look like a spider from a science fiction story and may be the larval stage of a lobster; and others that are totally transparent and look like beads lost from a plastic bracelet. These are all microscopic animals.

The drifting plants show less diversity and are generally of a more basically simple shape. There may be, for example, a stack of small perfectly proportioned poker chips that is a string of diatoms, or there may be a long chain of pretty green beads, a jack-straw pile of thin needles, a string of chinese lanterns, or a mass of Christmas-tree stars. Diatoms, however, are the main element of the phytoplankton in the global sea, and they have been counted in their natural state as thick as 220,000 per quart of seawater. It is the growth of these abundant yellow diatoms on the underside of whales in the Antarctic that has resulted in these whales' being called "sulphur bottom" by the whalers. These diatoms are so abundant that many parts of the ocean floor are composed almost completely of their quartz-like microscopic skeletons. In the few places where this diatom sediment, called diatomite, is now found on land, it is quarried and forms the fine abrasive power in most kitchen cleansers. The foraminifera, the pteropods, and the radiolarians are also abundant components of the plankton that have hard shells, and these too form distinctive bottom deposits.

However, not all of the plankton are microscopic in size. Since the plankton consists of the drifters—or at best the poor swimmers—they therefore also include the jellyfish and their various relatives. Some of the giant jellyfish may become as large as six feet across, with their dangling tentacles reaching out 25 feet beneath them to sting and capture their prey. There is no reason for the smallest things to have the longest names, but they seem to; and these small stinging cells are called neumaticists. They are very similar to the underwater swimmer's spear gun, being a sharp poisoned barb on a tightly coiled spring, which is shot out from along the filaments of the tentacles to inflict death on the unwary fish that comes into range. "By-the-wind sailor" is the name given to the transparent purple *Velella* that are often a conspicuous part of the open-sea plankton. These are flat discs that range up to four inches or more across. They float flat upon the sea, but have a transparent sail that rises above the water surface. On a smooth day at sea with a light breeze blowing, one will occasionally see a whole fleet of these "by-the-wind sailors" just scooting along as though they were a well organized race of one of the smallest classes of sail boats. In many cases, they also have a crew, for a small purple snail, *Jenthina,* evidently has some type of parasitic or symbiotic relationship with *Velella* and is often found attached to these little boats.

Organic production and "red tides." The abundant diatoms, though microscopic in size, are the most important producers of organic material in the sea. In the same way that plants on land are able to utilize sunlight, water, and carbon dioxide to produce carbohydrates and free oxygen, so too do the diatoms in the upper sunlit portions of the sea. These tiny drifting plants utilize the radiant energy of the sun in this same process of photosynthesis to produce and store vast amounts of energy as complex organic substances that become the source of chemical energy for the many and varied life processes in the ocean.

Although this process is the very basis of life in the sea and therefore of incredible benefit to mankind, it is a bit like breathing, in that you seldom think about it. It just goes on year in and year out without really impinging on your consciousness. Again, like breathing, it is only when something goes wrong with the mechanism, that you are suddenly made aware that the process even exists. The great plankton "blooms" that occur from time to time in the sea may be merely examples of incredibly accelerated organic production, or they may result from no great change in the rate of production, but rather from a temporary vanishing of the predators and physical factors that normally inhibit their abundance, so that the products of organic production just pile up. At any rate, these "blooms"—and that really is a most descriptive term for them—do occur. Probably the sighting of such a bloom in the Gulf of California led to its earlier name of the Vermilion Sea. The recurring blooms of small blue-green algae with the big name of *Trichodesmium erythraeum* impart the red color to the Red Sea. They also stirred a poet once to pen the immortal lines:

> We never quite believed him when the bug-man said
> That the blue-green algae make the Red Sea red.

If the diatoms are the most productive of the plankton, then the dinoflagellates are the second best producers. Biologists still argue as to whether these amazing organisms are plants or animals, but most oceanographers avoid the argument by considering that they lie just in between and are a little of each. The tiny one-celled dinoflagellate gets its name from the long whip, or flagella, with which it lashes back and forth to wiggle through the water. Thus it moves, like an animal, and some forms are predators and feed on even smaller forms of sea life. Certainly these are characteristics of a member of the animal rather than the plant kingdom. However, many of the dinoflagellates also contain the green pigment, chlorophyl, that enables them to utilize sunlight in photosynthesis, and this is characteristic of the plants rather than the animals.

Regardless of the problems raised in their classification, the problems raised by some of the dinoflagellate blooms are considerably more important to mankind. To this tiny creature have been traced the poisonous "red tides," those plankton blooms that result in the large mass mortalities of fish that are seen from time to time. In 1946 off the west coast of Florida such a "red tide" killed all manner of sea life and resulted in great windrows of dead and decaying fish along the shore. The smell became so bad that residents left the area and resort hotels had to close down.

It was very probably just such a phenomenon in the lower Nile centuries ago that is recounted in the Bible in the seventh chapter of the Book of Exodus ". . . . and all the waters that were in the river were turned to blood. And the fish that were in the river died; and the river stank, and the Egyptians could not drink of the waters of the river." Biblical scholars have for years assumed that this red coloring of the Nile was red mud brought down the river in flood stage from the red soils of Ethiopia. A "red tide," however, seems to provide a more logical explanation, for the killing of fish and the resulting smell are typical end products of a dinoflagellate bloom. Although the floods of the Nile are a common—almost annual— occurrence, they are not accompanied by any mass mortality of the fish population.

Dinoflagellates have also been tagged as responsible for some of the cases of shellfish poisoning in humans. They can be lethal, but not all species are toxic. What causes these sudden blooms, and what is there about these tiny creatures that is so lethal?

The sudden explosive reproduction of certain species of plankton may in some instances be related to a sudden enrichment of the waters by nutrients brought up from depth by the process known as upwelling. This most commonly occurs when a change in the coastal wind pattern moves the surface waters offshore, and the cooler nutrient-rich waters well up from below to replace them. Presented with this sudden superabundance of dissolved food, the dinoflagellates multiply at a rate much faster than normal. On the other hand, some investigators have felt that an unidentified nutrient material supplied by inflowing rivers might support the explosive growth, for the occurrence of such blooms off the mouths of rivers is common. However, an interesting bit of research off the mouth of the Fraser River in British Columbia showed that, although the bloom was in fact limited to the area of the Fraser River water on the surface of the sea, it was not some magic river-borne nutrient that caused the growth. It was found that the thin film of fresh river water lying on the surface of the sea induced a stable vertical stratification in the water. This meant that the usual turbulence was missing, and it was this vertical turbulence that normally carried many of the tiny plants below the depth where they could utilize sunlight and reproduce. Thus the main factor limiting abundant or explosive growth was removed, and the surface of the sea became a thick slurry of these organisms.

The nature of the toxins produced by the dinoflagellates has recently come under careful scrutiny because of the increasing use of various toxic substances, such as curare, in the study of the physiology of the human nervous system. Dinoflagellate poison acts on the nervous system by blocking the nerve impulses that tell the muscles to contract. Unable to move their gills or other muscles, the fish soon die. Perhaps continued research on this, one of nature's most virulent poisons, will in the end contribute much more to man's well-being than could ever be imagined if you happened to be on the west coast of Florida during those weeks in 1946.

The great abundance and variety of life in the global sea is most intimately interrelated with all other aspects of the sea—its currents and tides, the depth of the water and even the type of bottom sediment, the amount of light penetration, the temperature and salinity, the amount of dissolved nutrients and dissolved gasses; even the density of the water is important. But this is an *inter*relationship. Thus the decaying animal life returns to the sea as nutrients the material it removed for sustaining life, the shells of many of the planktonic organisms constitute a large percentage of the bottom sediments, and the photosynthesis of the drifting plants in the upper sunlit portions of the sea constitutes the major source of the dissolved oxygen in seawater. Even as the sea and the land are parts of one global unit, so too the various facets of the sea—its geology, its physics, its life, and its chemistry—are all merely parts of one immense system that becomes more and more fascinating as those who make its study their life work learn more of how it acts.

6   *The Amazing Liquid*

THE ocean somehow demands the use of superlatives in its description. It does indeed cover the largest part of the earth's surface, the trenches are in fact the largest features on earth, and the sea actually does contain the greatest amount of life on the planet.

Even the water requires the use of the superlative, for it is the most amazing liquid on the earth. If water were comparable to the other known liquids, it would, for example, boil at about minus 150° and freeze at about minus 240°F, instead of at the familiar temperatures of 212° and 32°F. Imagine, for example, what the consequences might be if, like most other substances, the solid state of water were heavier than the liquid state. Ice would sink instead of floating. Thus, instead of there being floating icebergs or drifting pack ice, the sea would long ago have filled with ice that had formed at the surface and sunk to the bottom. Oceanic circulation would have been interrupted, our climates would have been different, and in all probability life as we know it would never have evolved.

Other properties also make water a singularly strange liquid. It has, for example, the highest capacity for retaining heat of all liquids and all solids, with the single exception of liquid ammonia. This property of water prevents any extreme ranges in the temperature of seawater and means that heat transfer during the movement of water by currents within the sea is very large. Water also has the highest surface tension of all liquids. This is particularly important with respect to the individual cells of organisms, but is also critical in the formation of drops and other surface phenomena. Water in general dissolves more substances and in greater amounts than any other liquid, and this characteristic is of the utmost importance in the sea. To these unique qualities of water, man owes his very existence upon the earth.

DISSOLVED SALTS

Seawater was once defined as a dilute solution of almost everything, and this perhaps is one of the best definitions for it yet devised. It is a highly complex solution of dissolved solids, both organic and inorganic, and of gases. Over the centuries, the sea has been the earth's catchment basin, collecting all the elements that have been eroded from the continents, carried into the rivers, and eventually brought down in solution to be dumped into the sea. Add to this the material, both solid and gaseous, that has been ejected by underwater volcanoes, the material blown in from the land, the material of meteoritic origin, and the material produced by biological activity within the sea, and it is easy to see that the global sea is in fact a dilute solution of almost everything. In addition to its complex make-up, the dissolved solids in seawater constitute an amazing total amount of material. It has been calculated that if the dissolved material in the sea were removed and spread out over all the land, it would form a layer more than 500 feet thick.

Still, within this apparent chaos of more than 5 quadrillion metric tons of dissolved material, there is an amazing uniformity. As the result of the now classic 77 determinations of the chemical composition of seawater made on samples collected by the British *Challenger* Expedition in the nineteenth century, it was discovered that, although the *total amount* of the material dissolved in the sea may vary from place to place, there was essentially no variation in the *relative* amounts of the various substances dissolved. Except in the immediate areas of high run-off from the land, where the concentration of certain elements may be temporarily increased, the dissolved salts in the sea are in constant and known ratios one to the other. The total dissolved salts, or salinity, is lower where rainfall is abundant, where fresh water runs in, or where ice is melting, and higher in areas of high evaporation such as in some coastal lagoons or in partially enclosed seas where rain and run-off from the land are low or non-existent.

The general average salinity for the global sea runs at just a bit under 35 parts of dissolved salts per thousand parts of seawater. Since the ratios of the dissolved salts are constant, this means that the total salinity in any seawater sample can be determined by measuring only one of the constituents and then multiplying by a known factor to get the total dissolved salts. The chlorine content is normally used for this, since it is the most abundant element in seawater (about 19 parts of chlorine per thousand parts of seawater of average salinity), and the determination of the chlorine content is considerably less difficult than for most of the other elements. Using this technique over the years, oceanographers have obtained many determinations of the salinity of seawater. Not only is the general horizontal and vertical distribution of salinity fairly well known, but salinity has proven to be one of the means whereby oceanographers are able to "tag" a certain water mass and follow it as it moves through the ocean.

Variations in salinity. Variations in surface salinity of the open sea are small; the range is generally between 34 and 36 parts per thousand. The salinity is at a minimum near the Equator, rises to a maximum at about the latitude of the Tropic of Cancer in the northern sea (about on a line between Havana and Honolulu) and that of the Tropic of Capricorn in the southern sea (about on a line between Rio de Janeiro and the Tonga Trench). From there surface salinity decreases toward the polar regions. This north-south variation in surface salinity follows almost exactly a north-south variation in the difference between evaporation and rainfall, to which it is undoubtedly related. Because these causal factors are limited to the surface of the sea, most of the salinity variation is limited to the upper layers; and the deeper layers, though somewhat higher in salinity, are much more uniform with respect to the total amount of dissolved salts.

This is the general or average picture, but within it are the small-scale variations that make the picture really interesting. For example, salinity when combined with temperature can be used as a very useful means of keeping tabs on a particular mass of water. It is known, for example, that warm, high-salinity water formed in the eastern Mediterranean Sea flows out into the Atlantic through the Strait of Gibraltar along the bottom. Because of its greater salinity, it is denser and thus moves out underneath the less saline waters moving into the Mediterranean at the surface. This dense out-flowing water then sinks until it reaches an intermediate depth where the density is the same, and there it moves out. By measuring the temperature and the salinity of the water at depth, oceanographers have traced this Mediterranean water as far west as the Sargasso Sea and as far south as the southern tip of Africa.

In addition to working with the distribution of salinity—that is, with the variations in the *total* amount of the dissolved solids— marine chemists have also been at work trying to determine the *relative* amounts of the various individual dissolved elements. Over fifty have been identified and their concentrations determined. If you take the average of 35 parts of dissolved solids per thousand parts of seawater, there will be a bit over 19 parts of chlorine and a bit under 11 parts of sodium. These are the two constituents of the common table salt, and are the most abundant of the dissolved elements in the global sea. Next in abundance are magnesium with 1 part per thousand, sulphur with 0.9, calcium with 0.4, and potassium with a bit less than 0.4 parts per thousand. From there it ranges down to radium, which has been measured at 0.00000000000003 parts per thousand parts of seawater.

Gold is there too, and its concentration is about 0.000000004 parts per thousand. This may not seem like much, but when the volume of water in the entire global sea is considered, it amounts to between five and six million tons of gold. Assuming a price of $35 per ounce, the total worth of the gold dissolved in the sea can be quickly computed by a simple multiplication and a very large supply of zeros. After the first World War, the German chemist, Fritz Haber, thought that he could extract enough gold from seawater to repay

Germany's war debt and the famous *Meteor* Expedition of 1925-1939 was in part motivated by the need to secure more data for this worthy effort. Needless to say, no practical method has as yet been devised to recover any of this immense treasure of dissolved gold.

DISSOLVED GASES

All of the atmospheric gases are also found dissolved in seawater. Unlike the dissolved solids, however, the relative concentrations of the gases do not remain constant; they vary considerably. Dissolved oxygen, for example, varies from none at all to about 8.5 parts per thousand (normally given as milliliters per liter of seawater). In stagnant basins, such as some of the Norwegian fjords, below the depth of the threshold between a basin and the sea, the supply of dissolved oxygen may be completely used up in the decomposition of organic matter. These stagnant bottom waters typically have the "rotten-egg smell" of hydrogen sulfide. At other places, where abundant phytoplankton have increased the amount of photosynthesis in the upper sunlit regions, the dissolved oxygen concentration may be near the upper limits for the sea.

All of the dissolved oxygen in seawater gets into the water either directly from the atmosphere at the surface of the sea or else by the photosynthetic production of plants in the upper layers where adequate sunlight penetrates. Thus you would expect to find high surface values for the dissolved oxygen concentration. Below the area where the sunlight is adequate for photosynthesis, you would think that the oxygen supply would decrease steadily to the bottom as it got farther and farther from the source and was more and more used up by organisms and in the chemical decomposition (oxidation) of the dead organic material sifting down through the water.

What actually happens, however, has provided oceanographers with one of the great clues to the movement of water deep within the ocean. From the higher dissolved-oxygen values in the surface waters, the concentration does indeed decrease with depth as you would expect. Nearer the bottom, however, it suddenly increases again. Since there is no source for oxygen down there, and it must enter the water at or near the surface, there is no conclusion possible other than that these waters now at great depths obtained their oxygen when these same waters were actually at the surface. These waters, then, must have moved into the deep sea from somewhere on the surface. This was strong evidence for some sort of a vertical circulation pattern on an ocean-wide scale.

Since dissolved oxygen is utilized at depth, it would be logical to assume that the deep waters that had come the farthest would show the least oxygen, and those that had just left the surface would have the most. Thus it was postulated that the distribution of dissolved oxygen in the deep sea might be used to learn something about both the "age" of the deep water and the routes whereby the surface waters move down into the deep sea. Continued study of the distribution of dissolved oxygen in the deep waters showed a definite pattern. The waters richest in dissolved oxygen, and therefore believed to be the "youngest," were found in two places: around the Antarctic Continent and in the western North Atlantic. The concentration in the other deep parts of the ocean was found to diminish with distance away from these two points, so these are apparently the only areas where large amounts of surface water are sinking.

The deep temperatures seem to confirm this idea of a slow, sluggish flow of water at depth. Bottom water temperatures are very close to the freezing point. They do not seem to become warmed by downward mixing of the warm surface waters, so the assumption is that there is a continued renewal of these deep cold waters that in effect buoy up the surface waters. It is possible that these deep currents also show an intensification along the west sides of the bottom of the ocean basins in the same way the surface currents do to produce the Gulf Stream and the Kuroshio. In 1957 the British *Discovery* and the American *Atlantis* worked together seaward of Charleston, South Carolina, and did measure a southward-flowing current at a depth of 6,500 feet below the northward-flowing Gulf Stream. Velocities were between two and eight miles per day. However, many more measurements of the deep circulation will have to be made before the overall pattern suggested by the dissolved-oxygen distribution can be described with numbers rather than by such terms as "a slow, sluggish flow."

WATER TEMPERATURE

The variations in the temperature of the waters of the global sea, along with the salinity, the dissolved-oxygen concentration, and other variables, provide valuable clues to the processes that take place in the ocean. Because of water's amazing capacity for retaining heat once it has absorbed it, the variations in the temperature of the sea are much less than those for the land areas. Where temperatures over the land may range between less than −70°F to over 120°F, the range of temperature in the sea runs from a high of about 80°F to a low of 28°F. Whereas day and night differences in temperature of the land are generally high, nowhere in the sea is this daily variation more than about 1°F, and even the seasonal variation is seldom more than 10°F at any one place. Since the sea's temperature is determined by the amount of incoming solar heat, the distribution of surface temperature in the ocean, as on the lands, reflects the uneven distribution of the sun's heat; it is highest in the equatorial regions and lowest in the polar areas.

Vertically, the ocean waters are almost everywhere warmer at the surface, and the temperature drops off with depth to become very cold at the bottom. As with most other aspects of the study of the sea, it is the specifics rather than the generalities that are the more interesting. Off the west coast of Baja California, Mexico, a basin was found that did not follow the generality of decreasing temperature with depth. The waters did become cooler with depth to a point about 10 feet above the bottom, and there the temperature suddenly and unaccountably rose by about 2°F. Since water is lighter when it is warm than when it is cold, this bottom water should have risen to the surface. Was there a heat source down there, or was something keeping this water down on the bottom? When the salinity was measured, it was found that this thin layer of bottom water had an extremely high salinity—much higher than any normally encountered in the ocean. The basin where this layer was found lies just seaward of Scammons Lagoon, the same lagoon where the gray whales come each fall. What had happened was that extremely high evaporation along this desert coast had evaporated so much water from the shallow head of the lagoon that the salts left behind had greatly increased the salinity of the warm lagoon water. This water, even though warm, was very heavy because of its high content of dissolved salts, and sank to run along the bottom and out into the offshore basin, much the same way the more saline Mediterranean water moves out into the Atlantic. Thus the water found at the bottom of the basin was also very dense water and so remained there even though it was warmer than the overlying basin water.

The seasonal layer. A rapid vertical change in temperature is called a *thermocline,* and very shallow thermoclines can often be detected by swimmers who swim below the warm surface coastal waters and encounter a sharp transition to colder water a few feet below the surface. This is a thermocline, although a very shallow and probably quite transient one. In the open ocean, however, there is an upper layer of varying depth that is referred to as the *seasonal layer*—that is, the layer in which the seasonal changes take place and below which there are no appreciable changes on an annual basis. At the base of this layer is a marked decrease in temperature called the main or permanent thermocline, for it is almost always found everywhere in the sea. Above the main thermocline and within the seasonal layer occur the regular changes in temperature that are so well known that in many places in the sea a rough estimate of the month can be made merely by taking the ocean's temperature down to about 500 feet. In the early summer, as the surface of the sea begins to show the effects of continued heating, a shallow, sharp thermocline develops between the warmed surface waters at the very top of the seasonal layer and the unwarmed waters below. As the summer progresses, heating continues to warm the upper waters, but vertical mixing has extended the depth of the warm layer, and the thermocline moves down. This process continues until the surface temperature reaches a maximum in the early fall, and the thermocline is approximately at the middle of the seasonal layer. With winter cooling and winter storms, the surface temperature falls and the thermocline moves deeper until all the waters of the upper layer are at about the same temperature down to the depth of the main thermocline. Then the cycle starts all over again the next spring.

This regular cycle, of course, can be radically changed by a sudden storm in mid-summer. A storm extends the mixing to a greater depth and sets the stage for a secondary thermocline to develop. Often several of these rather abrupt changes may be present within the seasonal layer, and often slight temperature inversions occur, where for a time warm water underlies cooler water. This is the oceanic counterpart of the temperature inversions that are often found in the atmosphere. When cool air overlies warm air, this inversion often effectively traps the rising particles of man's contamination to form a smog layer. In the sea, too, these layers of water of different temperature often create what might be called underwater smog. Decaying organic material from a plankton bloom may be slowly drifting downward when it encounters a layer of colder, more dense water and may pile up there for a time. However, the recurring mariners' myth that there is a layer within the ocean below which a ship will not sink is just that—a myth. The density of any ship is so much greater than that of the water, even of the coldest and saltiest water, that once it has sunk beneath the surface, it will not come to rest at some intermediate depth. There is no mid-depth where we can expect to find all the ships that have ever sunk. If you want to look for them, you will have to go all the way to the bottom!

A useful indicator. Seawater temperature measurements provide a useful tool for the study of the sea. Gulf Stream water, for example, can be spotted easily by the sudden change in temperature from the cooler coastal water to the 80°F water of the northward-flowing current. Knowing that this so-called "cold wall" is on the left as you face down-current can be a valuable bit of information to the skipper of a sailboat in the Newport to Bermuda race, particularly if he encounters eddies and offshoots that could not have been predicted.

It was also by surface-water temperatures that oceanographers recently found an interesting area of upwelling off the east coast of Florida. Because seawater temperatures are taken almost daily at the tide stations of the U.S. Coast and Geodetic Survey, the annual variation in coastal water temperature is well known all along the Atlantic coast. For almost all stations, the pattern is exactly the same when observations over a long period are used to obtain average monthly values for the temperature of the sea surface. From a low in mid-winter, the graphs of the water temperature rise in a smooth arc to a high in September and then fall off steadily to the winter low.

The curves are all smooth except for those at Daytona Beach and Canova Beach along the Florida coast. At these two stations, the long-term average showed that the smooth rise in average monthly temperatures was interrupted by a sudden drop in water temperature during July and August. In 1951, for example, the drop was over 10°F between the monthly averages for June and July. Normally the ocean is warming up during this period, so the oceanographers began to look into the data to see what was causing this sudden early-summer appearance of cold water. By working with the long-term weather data, they discovered that along this particular stretch of coast the average wind direction makes a shift in July and August. During these two months the prevailing winds change to a direction that tends to move the surface waters offshore. Thus the colder surface waters along the coast during this period result from cooler waters welling up to replace the surface waters that were being blown seaward. The phenomenon had been there right along year after year, but it was not until adequate temperature data were available that it could be detected. So oceanographers will keep right on obtaining the temperature and salinity data that they need to help them understand what is happening in the amazing waters of the global sea.

MANY SCIENCES UNITED

Although an oceanographer may consider himself primarily a marine geologist, marine physicist, biologist, or chemist, he is forced by the very nature of the ocean itself to be a little of each. The various disciplines of geology, physics, biology, and chemistry may be quite separate in the catalogues of the various institutions of higher learning, but in the sea they are all delightfully intermingled.

As an example of this scientific *pot pourri,* take the microscopic foraminifera. There are hundreds of species that have been identified, but for the purpose of the example consider only the ones that form part of the plankton and construct the tiniest of perfect shells of calcium carbonate. These are animals, so the study of their life cycle and of their relationship with the environment properly falls within the realm of biology. Some of them are warm-water forms, some are cold-water forms, and still others are found throughout the sea, so the study of ocean currents immediately becomes involved in their distribution. Once the organisms die, the shells start the long voyage from the upper layers to the bottom of the sea. However, their shells of calcium carbonate can become dissolved as they sink into deeper waters that are cold and unsaturated with respect to calcium carbonate. Thus the involved physical chemistry of the carbonate system in the sea is brought into the picture. In those areas where the shells reach the bottom without dissolving, they can become the major constituent of the bottom sediments. One group of foraminifera, called the globigerinids, are the main component of the globigerina ooze that covers better than 50 percent of the floor of the Atlantic, Indian, and South Pacific oceans. This brings in the marine geologist.

All of these scientific fields were brought together in a recent study of some sediments obtained from the bottom of the Atlantic by a long coring tube that retrieved a vertical plug of the sediments covering the ocean floor. Since the rate of accumulation of sediments in the deep sea is usually very slow, a vertical plug of sediments 15 or 20 feet in length can be expected to represent a very long period of the history of that particular place. This core was composed primarily of foraminifera, and samples for microscopic study were removed from the core at regular intervals of depth. This meant that the sample taken from the top was the youngest and represented present-day conditions, and that the successively deeper samples were older and older, representing conditions in the sea longer and longer ago.

As he worked with these samples, the oceanographer found that there appeared to be two different assemblages of these microscopic animal shells. One was composed predominantly of the rather thin, delicate shells of species today found mainly in warm waters, whereas the other was composed of the thicker-shelled forms more typical of cold water. By determining the relative percentages of warm and cold water forms in each sample, he was able to get a relative indication of the changes in the oceanic water temperature over the long period recorded in that particular core. It developed that over much of the time represented by the core, the water had been very nearly the same temperature as it is now, for warm-water forms similar to those at the surface of the sediment core were found over much of its length. However, the cold-water forms seemed to dominate during four quite separate and distinct parts of the core, and the obvious implication is that in the past there were four periods when the surface waters of the sea were considerably colder than they are now. From geological evidence on land, the presence during the Pleistocene period of four separate advances of continental glaciers has been well established, the last one about 12,000 years ago. Most probably the four periods of cold water indicated by the foraminifera in that core represented a sea-floor record of this same glaciation.

It is in this way that oceanographers are opening up the pages of the history book that has been written on the floor of the ocean, but this is possible only when it is realized that the sea cannot be studied just from the geological or just from the biological, physical, or chemical point of view. All of the earth sciences meet in the sea, and all must be considered when investigating the various problems posed by the global sea.

7   *Our Last Resource*

Over the centuries man has learned a good deal about the global sea; this cannot be denied. As he has learned, however, he has come to realize just how intimately his very existence upon the land is tied in with his world-girdling ocean. The present resurgence of marine survey and research work is the result of this growing awareness that the sea is man's last great resource on this earth. It is indeed a great resource; but like other resources it must be mapped, it must be understood, and it must be utilized with the efficiency and care that come from understanding and without which it will be another of Earth's resources that man has used unwisely. In this case, however, it will be his last. The potential of the global sea as a resource for the improvement of man's well-being is almost as large as the mind of man can conceive.

MAPPING THE SEA

Before a newly discovered ore body can be developed fully, it must be mapped. Before a large area of forest can be effectively utilized as timber, the area must be mapped and the trees marked that are to be cut out. Before a dam can be built to store water for irrigation or for developing hydroelectric power, the entire watershed must be mapped. As any new frontier is opened up, the surveyors and mappers must move right along with the pioneers to prepare the basic maps on which will be based the future development of the land and its resources.

The greatest part of the land is now well covered by maps of various types. Every aspect of the lands in which man has any interest has been mapped, and this covers the gamut from the shape of the land with its high mountains, its rivers, its plains, and its coasts, to the distribution over the land of such things as rainfall, vegetation, soil types, faunas, the density of human population, the probability of earthquake damage, and even the susceptibility of various areas to a new advertising slant developed to insure the marketability of some new product. The point is that maps are an absolute necessity for showing where things are so that someone else can get to them. They are needed to show the distribution of anything that varies in quantity or quality from place to place on the earth. However, accurate maps of the ocean just do not exist outside the coastal areas. Even much of this nearshore area is inadequately mapped for safe commerce. The present condition of our maps of the sea is a direct reflection of the slowness with which we have come to realize the importance of this part of our earth. Now we need these maps, so we must start almost from the beginning to produce accurate base maps of nearly three-quarters of the surface of the earth.

With the post-war development of rugged, dependable echo-sounding equipment for survey work, we now have the basic tool for determining the water depth—or the height of the bottom, depending on your frame of reference. With the more recent development of long-range electronic navigational systems, we now can get accurate positions in the open sea in those relatively few areas covered by these systems. A good satellite navigation system is almost here. When it becomes a reality, we will be able to get accurate locations for the survey ship's position at any place on the earth's surface. Then a full-scale international effort to map the global sea will be undertaken, if plans now being laid come to fruition. In the meantime, a start is being made, but it is only a start—and a pitifully small one at that.

The Ocean Survey Program. On February 22, 1961, the U.S. Coast and Geodetic Survey Ship *Pioneer* steamed out through the Golden Gate at San Francisco to make the first trial run on the Ocean Survey Program, as it is called. This relatively unnoticed departure was the result of a program proposed in 1960 by the U.S.

National Academy of Sciences Committee on Oceanography. The translation of this basic program into the operational framework of the various governmental agencies that would be involved had been quickly carried out by the then newly formed Interagency Committee on Oceanography. It involved the conversion of a dream into the hard reality of ships, equipment, operational schedules, and—most important—men with the knowledge and love of the sea to carry out the great experiment.

Up until that day in 1961, oceanographic expeditions into the deep sea had been primarily reconnaissance expeditions or special cruises to investigate some specific oceanic feature, such as the deep currents investigated by the *Discovery* and *Atlantis* to test a theory. The *Pioneer,* however, was to carry out for the first time a systematic survey of the deep sea. A long series of north-south lines at intervals of 10 miles had been laid out well in advance to cover part of the vast and relatively unknown area between the Hawaiian Islands and the Aleutian Chain. This is one of the few oceanic areas covered by the land-based Loran-C system for determining ships' positions, and it was only because of this navigational innovation that such a survey was possible. This was to be more than just a routine charting of the ocean's depth, however, and the *Pioneer* was literally packed with scientists and technicians representing many different aspects of marine science and many different government agencies and private oceanographic institutions.

The basic philosophy underlying the operation was two-fold: the data must be highly accurate, and the ship must be utilized to obtain the maximum amount of information possible. The latter was accomplished by having aboard, in addition to the marine surveyors and oceanographers, and marine geophysicists from the Coast and Geodetic Survey, several marine geologists from the Geological Survey, marine biologists from the Bureau of Commercial Fisheries, and meteorologists from the Weather Bureau. There were also aboard marine botanists from the University of Hawaii who were interested in obtaining measurements of the productivity of the phytoplankton, and there was a marine radiochemist from the

Scripps Institution of Oceanography who made measurements of the amount of radioactive Cesium-137 [1] in the surface and deep waters of the North Pacific.

The *Pioneer* utilized every available bunk, square foot of laboratory and deck space, and hour of the day in an attempt to map not only the shape of the ocean bottom, but also the distribution of the anomalies in the earth's gravitational and magnetic fields. These characteristics do not change appreciably with time. Once the map was made, it would stand as a base map. In addition, the *Pioneer* sampled and studied various other characteristics that do change with time and still others that required the ship to be stopped. These included the regular release of meteorological balloons to collect data on the upper atmosphere, measurements of the currents, salinity, temperature, dissolved oxygen, and animal and plant life in the waters, and the obtaining of sediment cores on which shipboard analyses were made of the sediment as well as the waters within the sediment in an effort to learn about the geochemical processes that might be taking place. Even samples of the rainwater were collected for determination of the radioactivity content, and samples of the minute particles suspended in the air were taken to determine what such particles might be made up of.

The primary result of the first attempt at the Ocean Survey Program was the production of accurate maps of the undersea topography and maps of the gravitational and magnetic fields over a part of the deep sea far from land. This was a start. It was a good start, and the results indicate that it is a worthwile project, but the enormity of the whole job is almost staggering. If the Pacific Ocean were a lake 10 miles across at the Equator, a 200-foot oceanographic survey ship would be only 2½ inches long, and the cable with which she sampled the bottom would be a thin strand of spider web over 17 feet in length. It will obviously take many of these 2½-inch ships to explore this 10-mile lake plus the Atlantic and the Indian lakes.

[1] Cesium-137 does not occur naturally in the sea. Rather it is a byproduct of atomic explosions; hence its present distribution gives an indication of the movement of ocean waters and the rate of diffusion of such material.

The job of mapping our ocean with basic surveys must be accomplished, for the resulting maps will form the necessary basis for all future utilization of this great resource.

IMPROVED WEATHER FORECASTS

Within the ocean lies the key that will unlock the riddle of our weather on land. Of all the natural phenomena on this planet, probably weather and its long-term cousin, climate, have the greatest influence on the affairs of mankind. This applies not only to the growing of man's foodstuffs, but to the basic habitability of all parts of the earth. The science of meteorology has reached the point where the basic physical laws that govern the atmosphere are now fairly well known. The basic laws that govern the interaction of the sea and the overlying atmosphere are similarly known to a fair degree. What are now needed are the basic numbers that the global meteorologist can crank into his big electronic computers, and 71 percent of these numbers will have to come from the global sea. The reliable prediction of anything depends on knowing how the thing you are trying to predict varies in relation to whatever it is that is causing it. If you also know *why* one causes the other, it gives you more confidence in your predictions, but strictly speaking it is not necessary. However, in meteorology as in most other fields of science, so many variables enter into producing the end product that you really have to know the "why's" and "how's" of the whole complex process just to be able to tell what to measure at the other end to use in your predictions.

The influence of the global sea on our atmospheric circulation is a most important aspect of the air-sea interaction, and the possibility of long-range weather predictions is in a large measure dependent upon our better knowledge of this interaction. There are probably three major ways in which the sea affects the atmospheric circulation. One of these is the seasonal storage of heat in the ocean. The land, because of its low thermal conductivity, is unable to store heat for any period of time, but gives it back to the atmosphere almost as fast as it comes in.

The ocean, on the other hand, acts as a great heat reservoir and, because the surface temperature of the ocean changes little with the seasons, there is relatively little seasonal variation in the transfer of heat to the overlying atmosphere. This produces a stabilizing effect on the atmospheric circulation.

Another effect of the ability of the sea to store heat is the maintenance of a pattern of zonal heating of the atmosphere related to the pattern of the distribution of the ocean water and land masses. The meteorological implications of this zonal heating of the atmosphere involve the location of convergences and divergences in the moving air with their attendant low-pressure and high-pressure zones. They also involve strong horizontal temperature gradients in the air where the land and the sea meet, and these in turn affect the vertical stability of the air.

The ocean's ability to transport large quantities of heat from one part of the globe to another by means of sea currents also enters the picture by affecting certain minor aspects of the atmospheric circulation. For example, when there is an anomalous change in the amount of incoming radiation from the sun, the direct effect on the atmosphere itself may be relatively small and of brief duration because of the small capacity of the air to retain heat and the high velocities with which the air masses move. The sea, on the other hand, has a much longer "memory" for these things because of its high heat capacity and the slowness of its currents compared with those in the atmosphere. The point to be made from all of this is that the global sea is of prime importance to the atmospheric circulation; it is the great "flywheel" of the engine that drives our planetary wind system.

When the complex system is thoroughly worked out and when enough data on the oceanic aspects of this system become available, then we will have the basic facts necessary for working out a system of good long-range weather forecasting. Imagine the immeasurable benefit to mankind of having published each year for the following year an accurate day-to-day weather prediction even as we now can publish daily tide predictions years in advance.

WEATHER MODIFICATION

With knowledge comes understanding, and with complete understanding comes the ability to predict. By the same token, the ability to effect change often comes with this complete understanding. Mark Twain once commented that everyone talks about the weather, but no one does anything about it. Perhaps the day is not far off when weather control will be removed from the science-fiction category and into the realms of actuality.

Several possible methods for changing the distribution of climate or modifying the weather have been suggested in the past. One such plan consisted of covering the thin Arctic ice cap with carbon black to increase the absorption of solar heat with a consequent melting of the ice and a whole series of subsequent effects on the atmosphere. Many of these same effects might more easily be created, it has been suggested, by utilizing nuclear energy to throw large quantities of water into the Arctic air, where it would then freeze to create a vast ice cloud. This cloud would reduce the amount of infrared radiation returning to space and so decrease the amount of surface cooling. Other ideas have included the building of dams to divert ocean currents and the placing of nuclear-powered heat generators on the sea bottom to induce vertical circulation along the coasts and thereby rearrange the surface-temperature pattern. One scheme for giving rain to southern California and simultaneously removing the smog from the Los Angeles basin involved anchoring large barges offshore on which acres of nuclear-powered heating rods are just awash in the surface waters of the sea. The overlying heated moist air would then rise, move inland with the prevailing westerlies, be cooled as it was lifted up over the mountains where it would then drop its contained water as rain when the temperature was lowered past the dew-point. The rising air above the barges would cause air to move in along the surface of the sea to replace it, and this air flowing out of the Los Angeles Basin toward the barges would carry away the smog.

All of these are intriguing ideas, and some of them probably would work. However, the results might be considerably more discomforting to mankind than are the original conditions these schemes were designed to remedy. As with the understanding of the present meteorological aspects of the earth, these schemes for weather modification are dependent upon a thorough knowledge of the air-sea interaction to the extent that the planned changes will have totally predictable and desirable results. Perhaps this is stretching a bit the interpretation of the word "resource," but the possible benefits to accrue to mankind from long-range weather predictions and possible weather modification seem so great and are so dependent upon the global sea that their inclusion in a discussion of the sea as our last great resource seems justified.

FOOD FROM THE SEA

The rate at which man has been increasing his population on this planet is well known. There were about a billion humans in 1830. It had taken on the order of 10,000 years to reach this total, yet we had doubled this during the mere 100 years between 1830 and 1930. Just since 1930 we have added something over one more billion to the earth's population. Taking into consideration the various factors that contribute to the variations in the birth rate and the death rate, these figures from the past have been projected into the future with really frightening results. The current rate of growth would put over six billion people on the earth by the year 2000; and in 600 years there would be only one square yard of living space per person. One prediction has even gone so far as to foresee that in 6000 years the solid mass of human flesh would be expanding outward from the earth into space at the speed of light.

Obviously something will have to be done to curtail the rate of population increase, but in the meantime there is a rapidly increasing number of mouths that need to be fed. Improved methods of agriculture will help a good deal, and more people are being fed per acre of planted food every year; but the greatest relatively untapped source of food on earth lies in the global sea. The potential of this resource is undoubtedly more important to mankind than any other resource in the ocean.

Currently, man obtains only about 1 percent of his food from the sea, and possibly as much as 10 percent of his essential protein material. One percent of his food from 71 percent of his planet: this hardly seems like an equitable distribution. We know that there is a tremendous supply of unused food in the sea, and the beauty of this resource is that it is self-renewing. Unlike the fuel and minerals on the land, which are there in a finite amount and which once used up are forever gone, the supply of food in the sea continues to replenish itself. It is for this very reason, perhaps, that we must be especially careful not to overfish a certain species or a certain area. We must insure that this property of self-renewal is not destroyed in our eagerness to increase our supply of food from the sea. The practice of intelligent conservation must go hand in hand with increased utilization. The food in the sea may be self-renewing, but it is not indefinitely so against an all-out assault to increase our marine food production. The importance of intelligent conservation of this resource—as with all others—cannot be stressed enough. But what is this self-renewing resource, and what are some of the problems involved in its increased utilization?

Some 25,000 different species of fish (in the true sense, as opposed to the popular use of the term for any animal in the sea) have been identified from the ocean. Relatively few of these, however, are utilized as a commercial food source. Commercial fishing presently is limited to those species of fish that can be caught in quantities sufficiently large to be delivered to the consumer at a price that will allow each person along the line to make some profit out of the operation. It is a question, then, not only of the supply of fish, but of the economics of the whole process. Many fish that are not now utilized as food could be if fishing techniques were developed to capture them in large enough quantities.

In some areas of the world, increasing the total amount of fish delivered at the ports would not improve the food supply of the people unless the increase in fish were accompanied by some means to preserve it and transport it inland before it spoiled. In other parts of the world, fish are available, but the people happen not to like to eat fish when they can get other types of food that appeal to them more, so the size of the potential market would not justify the effort to increase the supply of fish in that area. We know that there are many more fish in the sea than are currently utilized, and we know that the take of most species of fish can be considerably increased without fear of overfishing. So the problem of increasing man's food from the sea is a complex one involving, among other things, the increasing of our knowledge of how and why the abundance of fish varies.

Prediction of available fish. The fluctuations in fish populations have always been a major headache to the commercial fisherman, and these fluctuations are still to a large extent unpredictable. The Norwegian herring is one of the classic examples of this. In the mid-nineteenth century, the annual catch averaged about 700,000 metric tons; yet shortly after 1900, the catch dropped to about 75,000 metric tons and remained at a low level for about 20 years. Then in 1925 the catch suddenly surged upward again to 600,000 metric tons. Comparable wild fluctuations have been encountered in most commercial species. The fisheries based on the Hudson River shad, the salmon, and the California sardine have all undergone periods of rapid expansion and just as sudden decline resulting from large fluctuations in the quantity of available fish. Causes for these fluctuations may range from the effects of overfishing, pollution, dams, and logging on the rivers that contain spawning grounds, to such natural causes as changes in the water temperature or other environmental factors, changes in the abundance of the plankton that form an important link in the food chain, or variations in the number of predators that feed on the particular fish you are after.

In spite of this array of variables, some degree of prediction of future abundances is even now possible. For example, the U.S. Bureau of Commercial Fisheries has found that the catches of tuna in the area around the Hawaiian Islands in recent years have been predictable with a high degree of reliability from the temperature data collected at Cocoa Head on Oahu. The reasons are not yet fully understood, but they are undoubtedly related to movements of large masses of water within the central Pacific.

Some minor success in prediction has been achieved by estimating the number of young in any given year and knowing how many years it will take before this year-class, as it is called, becomes the dominant fish in the catch. This method makes possible some prediction of variations in the yearly catch. A more accurate system is based on the age composition of the whole population whereby the size of any one year-class can be followed year after year until it ends up in the fishing boats. There also seem to be some quite regular cyclical variations in the total catch of some species, so that the population can be predicted with some assurance from the history of past catches. In certain other fisheries, and the North Pacific halibut is a good example, there appears to be a relatively constant number of young fish added to the population each year. With this relatively uniform annual source of new fish, the inference is that the available adult population will depend heavily on the mortality rate, and when this rate is known the available catch can be predicted.

Prediction of where to go for the fish is still in its infancy, because the factors that influence where the fish will be are still far from completely understood. Water temperature seems to be one characteristic that has some effect in determining which areas fish choose in preference to others. Abrupt changes in the water temperature present an almost impenetrable barrier to some fish. Off the tip of the prominent point that forms the southern boundary of Santo Thomas Bay at Ensenada on the west coast of Baja California, Mexico, there is such an abrupt change in the temperature of the water that temperatures as much as 11°F apart have been measured from opposite ends of the same small skiff. North and south of this "temperature wall," two completely different assemblages of fish are found. This is perhaps an extreme case, but it has been shown that temperature can be an effective indicator, and there are now being made available to the fisherman on the west coast of North America regular monthly charts showing the distribution of surface temperatures in the eastern Pacific, and these have been of help in locating schools of fish. The real clues, however, to predicting where the fish will be and how many of them will be available for catching will be known only when we know considerably more about the relation of the fish to their environment. This is a continuing research project, and it entails studying the environment as well as the fish. It entails surveys of the distribution of the environmental factors and of the fish; it entails laboratory experiments, life-history studies, population studies, fish-behavior studies, and then more work at sea to see if these studies have made any sense. It is a long job, but when it is completed we will be able to extract more of the fish from the sea.

Other foods from the sea. Obtaining more of the commercial fish from the sea is one method of increasing our utilization of this vast protein resource, but we should also look to the possible utilization of other than the standard marine food products with which we are already familiar. In other parts of the world, the muscles from the back of the ugly sea cucumber are a great delicacy, and the internal organs of the spiney sea urchin are considered really good eating. Octopus, squid, and certain seaweeds are eaten elsewhere, and the fish section of any foreign marketplace always contains some species that are totally unfamiliar to the tourist.

The plankton have been called the "pastures of the sea." They are in fact much more abundant than the pastures on land and may some day be harvested on a commercial basis as a food product. A sandwich made from the catch in a plankton net may be delicious if the net happens to be pulled through a thick concentration of young shrimp or small free-swimming crabs. On the other hand, the great proportion of sandwiches that might be made in this fashion would be totally inedible, for they would be made predominantly of considerably less palatable organisms such as small jellyfish, fish larvae and eggs, and a whole slurry of minute marine creatures that are anything but gourmet food. This in no sense means that the plankton should be ruled out as a good source, for by adequate processing or by the "aquaculture" of selected species, it could very possibly be used directly. More probably, it will be first used as a fertilizer for the soil in which more edible forms of food may be grown, or as a feed for some of the land animals that now are a source of food.

The commercial possibilities of a high-protein flour called fish meal are at present considerably brighter than those of the plankton. This meal is produced from the so-called trash fish and the leftovers from the processing of the commercial species. It is all completely dried and pulverized, and all of the "fish odor" is removed in the process to produce a neutral-tasting white protein concentrate. It obviates the problem of preservation, can be produced relatively cheaply, and is not recognizable as a fish product to those who might not like the taste of fish. The possibility is now being investigated of this product's being used to supplement the diet of the people in many parts of the world suffering from the ravages of protein deficiency.

Better understanding of the relation of the fish to his environment, improvement of the techniques for catching fish, utilization of marine products not now commonly used, development of new protein-rich byproducts, and improvement in the techniques for preserving and distributing the final product will all aid in increasing our food from the ocean. But again, they must all be combined with adequate methods of conservation so that the great self-renewing resource of the food in the sea will be available to feed the rapidly increasing numbers of people on this planet.

MINERALS FROM THE SEA

The economics of recovering sea resources is an important aspect of the fisheries problem, but it is the controlling factor in the recovery of the minerals dissolved in seawater. We know that the minerals are there, we know the amount of their concentration in seawater, and we know that the concentration is essentially the same regardless of where we get the seawater. The problem, then, reduces to the basic question of how to recover these dissolved minerals at a cost that makes it worthwhile. Although the problem can be simply stated, the solution is anything but simple for many of the dissolved elements.

Salts. Common salt, however, is amazingly simple to remove from seawater, and it is known that the Chinese obtained sea salt as early as 1,000 B.C. A gallon of seawater contains about a quarter of a pound of salt; the whole sea, about 4½ million cubic miles of it. Generally, salt is commercially removed from seawater by allowing the water at times of spring tides to flow into shallow diked basins. Here the suspended impurities settle out, and slight concentration of the brine may take place by evaporation of some of the water. The clarified brine is then run into a secondary basin, where continued evaporation of the water causes the first crystals to precipitate out. As the process of evaporation continues, more and more compounds will settle out of the thickening brine. Iron sulfide, calcium carbonate, calcium sulfate, and sodium chloride (table salt) are precipitated out of the brine at successively greater brine concentrations—that is, as the evaporation goes on over longer and longer periods of time. Thus the amount of time in any single evaporation basin is carefully controlled. What would otherwise be a single layered deposit of many different salts, one atop the other, becomes a series of thin layers on the bottom of many separate ponds. Each pond thus contains just those salts that are desired.

The most abundant salt recovered by this method is sodium chloride, which finds wide usage not only for seasoning food, but also for meat and fish packing, in canning and preserving and other food processing, in dyes and many other chemicals, in tanning leather, for livestock, water treatment, metallurgy, for refrigeration, and even in the processing of textiles and the manufacture of soap. For years the remaining bittern, or mother liquor, from the salt works was discarded; and, although most of it eventually found its way back to the sea, the volume of valuable chemicals lost through this practice was large. For example, the mother liquor remaining after the precipitation of 100,000 tons of salt contains

2,800 tons of potassium chloride, 27,300 tons of magnesium chloride, 16,000 tons of magnesium sulfate, and even 240 tons of pure bromine. Milk of magnesia and bath salts are also recoverable from these salt bitterns. During World War I when the price of chemicals skyrocketed, the recovery of these byproducts suddenly became profitable. As a result, the separation of these minerals was undertaken; and as technology improved, the cost of the separation was reduced. Today many byproducts are recovered from these bitterns that once were wasted, but again the problem is mainly economic.

Other dissolved resources. The direct removal of elements from seawater, as opposed to the removal of chemical compounds by evaporation, is a relatively recent development. In 1924 there was a sudden demand for increased amounts of bromine for use in gasolines, since the "ethyl" gasoline contained a bromine compound, and a pilot plant for extracting bromine from seawater was established on the Atlantic coast. In 1931 a second pilot plant was set up to see if the general methods of separating bromine from salt-pan mother liquors could be applied directly to seawater, and production reached about 500 pounds of bromine per day. Eventually these two test plants were combined into one large plant near Wilmington, North Carolina, where the extraction of bromine directly from seawater was carried out successfully on a commercial scale.

Metallic magnesium is also recovered directly from seawater, the first metal to be so recovered on a commercial basis. Calcium carbonate in large quantities is an essential ingredient of this process, so the first plant was located at Freeport, Texas, where great reefs of oyster shells were available in close association with plenty of seawater and a nearby river by which the "used" seawater could be carried off. This plant, and another like it, now turn out a total of about 125,000,000 pounds of 99.9-percent-pure magnesium each year.

As the dwindling supplies of the various metals are used up on land, we will be forced to turn to the sea for a continuing supply to meet our needs. These dissolved elements in seawater are one of our great resources on this earth, and they will be there when we need them. It needs only the ingenuity of man to devise the ways of getting them out, and as the scarcity of a land-derived material relative to the need sends the price up sufficiently, then the method for its recovery will be developed.

Manganese nodules. The recovery of minerals from the deposits at the bottom of the global sea presents a somewhat different problem, because these minerals are not evenly distributed as are the dissolved minerals in seawater. The most interesting accumulation on the sea floor, and probably the one that will eventually be most fully exploited, is the mineral lumps made up primarily of manganese, iron, nickel, cobalt, and copper, and called *manganese nodules.* These potato-like concretions of minerals were first dredged from the sea floor during the British *Challenger* Expedition in the last century. Since then has come the development of the deep-sea camera, and with this equipment we have found large areas of each of the three major arms of the global sea to be covered with these nodules. The largest one known to have been recovered weighed about 300 pounds and was brought up tangled in an undersea cable being retrieved for repairs. It was sketched and sampled, but unfortunately the men aboard were more interested in cables than in minerals, and the specimen was dropped back into the sea. The second largest known specimen was brought up by the research vessel *Horizon* of the Scripps Institution of Oceanography during an expedition to the Gulf of Alaska in 1951. The method of recovery was sufficiently interesting that it might be worthwhile to quote from a description of the recovery of this amazing sea floor specimen written at the time.

"Yesterday, though, things began to pop. My watch again had the night station the night of the 10th and 11th (September 1951), and Al Smith and José secured after the deep cast was in, and Bill Riedel came on deck to help me with the core. It was to be core No. 10. We put the rig over in 2750 fathoms of water—that is three miles straight down—and it would have taken 5000 meters had the wire gone straight down, but even though there was a very mild swell and the wind was light, we had a goodly drift that managed to work up a 45° wire angle by the time 5000 meters of wire were out, so we took her down some more to make up for the big wire angle. I wish some one would work out or discover what a wire suspended in water does as the ship drifts. It certainly doesn't stay at 45° all the way to the bottom. . . . We let out finally 6300 meters or all but the last layer of turns on the winch drum, and still the ball didn't pop. We had a hydrophone over and the volume turned up, but no blasted pop. We couldn't let out any more because 'there ain't no more,' so we started to haul it in and hoped we had a core. At 5900 meters the winch ground to a groaning complaining halt. Don Derringer was winch-man—full beard and now waxing the much-fingered almost micro-scopically small tips of his mustache—and I went up to the boat deck to check with him. He goosed up the power and the winch began to turn slowly, each roll to port putting enough strain on the thing to stop the winch. On the starboard roll a foot or so of cable would come up, and then the ensuing port roll would loosen enough so that the next roll back we could pull a bit more in. We had seen it do this before and knew it was the way a winch reacted when it was pulling a deep core out of the bottom, so our hopes rose. It would be a three-hour job at least—or should be if your wire has as many splices as this one has—to bring a core up from over three miles, so we settled down to some semi-serious dip-netting and spearing. There were a few large sauries that broke water occasionally in short jumps as they streaked around under the light. I saw one flying fish and a few three-foot white bellied devils just out of the range of good vision. Then the squids came up—probably after the sauries, and I missed eight of ten good ones with the spear.

"It was then early in the morning, Derringer had given way to Fenton on the winch, pitch black night had given way to the first faint subtle shadings of dawn, and my thoughts on fishing had given way to happy if somewhat libidinous thoughts of the girls back home, when I was startled by a splash followed by great dripping noises. I turned, and there where the wire left the water and rose past the bucket to the sheave, a great gleaming black mass clung to the wire and was still dripping as it rose slowly upward twisting lazily about the wire. I screamed at George to stop the winch and jumped into the bucket. What I had at first fleeting glimpse thought to be a turtle, I now saw was an immense rock that had somehow fouled in the $\frac{5}{32}$-inch wire we use for hydrographic wire and had been hauled all the way to the surface. The winch had stopped, and it seemed quiet without the usual straining whine that changes pitch with every roll, and I could hear the dripping as water still drained from 'the thing.' George shouted down 'What the hell is it, Stew?' I was looking at it and still couldn't believe it. Three or four turns of hydrographic wire were wrapped around it, and I held my breath for fear it would come loose and drop back into the water. Who would believe me when I told them that 'we brought up a big rock in the hydrographic wire, but it—ah—came off and fell back into the sea'? I knew at once that it was a real find and could now see that it was at least coated on top with MnO_2—manganese dioxide— a typical encrustation often found on rocks dredged from the ocean floor. Mid-Pac Expedition had gotten some nice nodules from Sylvania, Hess, and Johnson guyots, and they were ecstatic over specimens the size of your fist, and here before me dangling on a wire no bigger than a lead pencil was a piece almost three feet across. I shouted for Bill Riedel, and he came up into the bucket. We decided to have George raise it gently and we would pull it over and rest it on the edge of the bucket. Then the ship rolled, and I hung onto that thing for dear life. If it had gone to the bottom, I think I would still have been hanging on when it landed. Bob Haines brought the wire comealong, hooked it to the bucket rail, and took enough strain off the outboard part of the wire that we were able to unwrap the specimen, and Bill and I lowered it gently—even lovingly—to the floor of the bucket. It is without a doubt the finest geological specimen ever brought up from the ocean floor—certainly the biggest from that depth. It is the sort of specimen that should be placed on a pedestal in a museum somewhere with a brass plate identifying it, and a velvet guard rail on highly polished brass posts to keep people from touching it. We carried it into the lab, grinning like Cheshire cats. We knew it was a real trophy. . . ."

From dredge hauls and from bottom photographs, it is known that the average size of these manganese nodules is about that of the average potato, which they so closely resemble. Estimates of their concentration on the surface of the bottom are rough at best, but in an area of 16 million square miles in the eastern Pacific, the Institute of Marine Resources of the University of California has estimated that there are about 230 billion tons of these nodules. Manganese nodules are also found in the Atlantic, but they generally contain more iron and less manganese, nickel, cobalt, and copper than their Pacific counterparts. The Blake Plateau off the coast of the Carolinas and northern Florida has been found to be covered with abundant nodules ranging in depths of from 500 to 3000 feet. These are considerably shallower than are the great preponderance of the Pacific nodules, but they also assay out at lower values. Using 1961 prices, the value of the recoverable metals in manganese nodules ranges from $45 to $100 per ton of nodules.

Figures have been developed to determine the economics of getting manganese nodules up from the sea floor, and—at least on paper—the recovery appears to be feasible from both the engineering and the economic points of view. It now remains for some intrepid company to try it and see if the project is in fact feasible.

The origin of these strange mineral accumulations is not completely known. Most probably they result from the collection of colloidal particles of the various elements as they filter down through the water, the colloids of manganese and iron attracting those of nickel, copper, cobalt, and the other metals found. These colloidal particles carry electrical charges and are then attracted to any hard object on the bottom. Once started, the growth of the metal acts as a collecting agent for more of the same, and the nodules over the years build up. Another school of thought throws out this idea completely and ascribes the whole process to the activity of marine bacteria. Regardless of how they are formed, if the method of their formation can be determined, then it is possible that the same conditions can be reproduced in coastal lagoons where large amounts of seawater could be brought into the system to have the valuable elements removed. These would in effect be "metal farms." The idea may sound far-fetched, but once we know exactly how these nodules are formed, it may be possible. Continued research on these nodules will decide whether such a theme is practical.

Although the manganese nodule has somehow caught the public fancy, it is by no means the only mineral resource on the floor of the global sea. In 1961 the U.S. Department of the Interior opened for lease an area of sea-bottom deposits of phosphorite off the west coast of the United States, and the Collier Carbon and Chemical Company, a subsidiary of Union Oil Company of California, acquired some of this area on lease for the development of these deposits. Like manganese, phosphorite also occurs as nodules, but of irregular shape. Assays of the material found off the coast of California run about 28 percent P_2O_5, a good source of phosphorus. This element is essential for the growth of living cells, and the greatest use of phosphorite is in commercial fertilizers for replenishing the soil in heavily farmed areas. Elemental phosphorus is also recovered from phosphorite and is used in the manufacture of chemicals for such products as water softeners, detergents, leavening agents, and insecticides, and the phosphorus is used directly in the manufacture of matches, phosphorus alloys, and various military articles such as smoke shells, incendiary bombs, and the like.

Other minerals. Other sea-bottom minerals are not nearly so attractive at present for commercial development as are the manganese and phosphorite nodules, but others are known to exist in large quantities. Red clay covers about 40 million square miles of the sea floor, and, although its composition is quite similar to the average composition of igneous rocks on land, there has been a large enrichment of manganese, lead, molybdenum, nickel, copper, and cobalt. The globigerina ooze covering better than 50 percent of the floor of the global sea is as high as 95 percent calcium carbonate, the essential component of cement. Gold washed in from the land has undoubtedly accumulated on the shallow sea bottom near shore, and the recently organized minerals department of the Shell Oil Company has within the past year taken over a potential gold-producing area off the coast of Alaska. There are even diamonds on the sea floor, and a floating diamond digger is being built in South Africa that will dredge up 18,000 tons of diamond-bearing gravels per month.

Some marine organisms concentrate metals that are almost undetectable in seawater. Certain of the tunicates, the so-called "sea squirts" often found on pier pilings at low tide, have the amazing ability to filter out and collect the element vanadium to a concentration 50,000 times that in seawater. Even the common oyster concentrates 200-fold the copper it filters from the water, and some snails can concentrate lead. Perhaps in some future time, these animals too will be put to work in "metal farms," for the metals they collect comprise a portion of the vast storehouse of minerals that forms an important part of our last resource.

WASTE DISPOSAL

When man ushered in the Atomic Age, he opened up a whole new energy source for running his complex civilization. Granted, he is a bit slow about putting it aside as a tool of war and concentrating on its peaceful uses, but he had the same trouble when he found out about iron. "This is the end of civilization as we know it" was probably coined then, when man thought of the havoc to be wrought in his wars now that spear tips and swords could be made of this new material. Yet iron survived the war stage and now, as steel, it forms the very backbone of our industrialized way of life. So too with the nuclear reaction. When we accepted the Atomic Age, we also accepted—like it or not—the problem of what to do with the atomic waste materials that came with it. It is quite possible that one of the great resources of the sea is that it is a useful place to dump things that we do not want around on the land. Dredge hauls in the Florida Straits often recover clinkers that were dumped overboard years ago from passing steamships. The dumping of old automobiles and streetcars into piles on the continental shelf has not only gotten rid of these leftovers, but has also made excellent fishing spots. Municipal sewage from our coastal cities has traditionally been disposed of into the ocean, so the sea is in fact a good place to dump things. The problem then boils down to whether or not it is a good place to dump *all* things, but in this case the specific thing is radioactive waste material. But just what is this radioactive waste about which people tend to get so excited?

Radioactive wastes. Like "money," the term "radioactive waste" is a general term and does not specify how much of what denomination. And again like money, radioactive waste exists in a wide range of values. High-level wastes have been defined as those with "concentrations of hundreds or thousands of curies per gallon," while low-level wastes are those with "concentrations in the range of one microcurie per gallon." [2] The "curie" is a measure of the activity of a radioisotope and is approximately the rate of disintegration of one gram of radium, and the "microcurie" is one-millionth of this value. Thus the range of radioactivity from low-level wastes to high-level wastes is comparable to a money range of from one penny to millions or tens of millions of dollars.

Because of this tremendous range in the degree of radioactivity, there have developed two main approaches to the waste-disposal problem. The first is used for the high-level radioactive wastes, the ones more dangerous to man, and consists of their being concentrated and then contained somehow. The other approach is often used for the low-level and less dangerous wastes and consists of dilution and dispersal. Present practices generally call for the high-level and intermediate-level wastes to be contained in storage tanks on land, whereas low-level wastes are in some cases discharged either directly or after treatment into the ground, into rivers, or into the sea through long pipes, or else they are surrounded with concrete or put in sealed containers and disposed of at sea. Until such time as the containment of the high-level wastes is such that these containers can be placed on the bottom of the ocean without the slightest possibility of the contained material ever getting into the environment, the disposal of radioactive wastes at sea will be limited to the low-level wastes.

The radiation properties cannot be destroyed by any reversal of the method whereby they were originally produced. Someone once compared such an attempt to cutting the grass in the front yard by lying on your stomach and firing a .22 caliber rifle through the blades of grass. The waste material is definitely with us and will

[2] Hearings on Industrial Radioactive Waste Disposal, Joint Committee on Atomic Energy, Congress of the United States, 1959.

have to be disposed of. The sea has a great capacity for the dilution and dispersal of contaminants. There is little doubt of this, but we must know just *how* great; we have to be able to put the numbers into the formulas. These numbers are not now available for the sea. We do not even know the rate at which surface waters move down to become the bottom waters. We do not know the rate at which various marine organisms might take up these radioactive elements in much the same way mollusks take up calcium for their shells or "sea squirts" concentrate vanadium. We do not have numbers yet for the actual rates of diffusion in the sea, and the scale of these diffusion phenomena varies from the very small-scale molecular diffusion, which causes one drop of ink in a glass of water soon to color the whole glass, to the larger-scale turbulences, whose effective size is even unknown. Then to the diffusion must be added the whole advection process, the process whereby waters containing the wastes are physically moved from one part of the ocean to another, both vertically and horizontally. We do not know all of these rates. This really is a long way of saying that we do not yet know very much about what paths individual molecules of various compounds take through the waters, animals, and sediments of the sea. Some of this type of information is becoming available. The U.S. Atomic Energy Commission, for example, has been supporting basic research in the fields of oceanic circulation, uptake of elements by organisms, ion exchange between the ocean water and the sea-floor sediments, and other research projects which might produce information that will be of use in evaluating the sea as a disposal site for radioactive waste products. We must know.

The real point to be made is that if the sea is to continue as a resource for anything other than dumping radioactive wastes, it is absolutely essential that we continue our studies of the sea. Insofar as waste disposal is concerned, we should continue these studies until we know just how much of what type of radioactive material can be put in where without endangering mankind or destroying other resources within the sea that we might need more than we need a radioactive dump. Work on this problem is going on now. A useful hole to dump things in may be one of the global sea's great resources, but we just do not yet know.

FRESH WATER

Of all the resources of the global sea, the most abundant one is water itself—some 300 million cubic miles of it. If this water were distributed evenly among the people of the world today, each would receive more than 100 billion gallons of salt water. There is even a good deal of fresh water on the earth, although most of it is locked up in glaciers; but if this were evenly distributed it would provide about a billion gallons of fresh water per person. The "water problem," then, that confronts the world today is not one of insufficient total water, but rather primarily a problem of distribution. It is doubtful that we will ever be able to increase the total amount of water on earth, so we must concentrate on the more effective use of the vast amounts we have. As the population increases, there will be ever-increasing demands for fresh water, not only for drinking, which takes a relatively small portion of the available fresh water, but for agriculture, which takes some 50 percent of it (not counting the rain used directly by the growing plants), and for the increasing industrial and municipal uses.

In the United States we already have a serious water problem. This has come about from a variety of factors, but the main ones are the growing population, with the resultant migrations into the more arid parts of the country, the increased volumes of water used by each person as the general standard of living improves, and the extension of irrigation in most parts of the country. In 1900, for example, the total daily use of fresh water in the United States was about 40 billion gallons. By 1940 this had more than tripled to 135 billion gallons, and in 1960 it had risen to over 300 billion gallons per day.

The problem is not one that is limited to the United States. The same causes in the other industrialized countries of the world have resulted in similar water shortages. In the newly emerging countries, many of which are in semi-arid regions with a constant water shortage, the recent introduction of modern sanitary and medical practices has increased the demands on the available water. The growing lack of an adequate supply of fresh water in most parts of the world today has indeed become a problem. The steadily increasing need for more and more water makes the problem an even greater one for the future. The conversion of salt water from the global sea into fresh water for the use of man, his agriculture, and his industries is one of the most promising uses of this great resource.

Fresh water from the sea. Desalination—the conversion of salt water to fresh water by removing the dissolved salts—is not a new idea. For over two centuries man has been able to extract fresh water from seawater by distillation. This merely involves boiling seawater, and collecting and condensing the resulting steam to provide fresh water. This is an excellent technique for providing high-quality fresh water, but the fuel costs make it prohibitive on a large scale if the cost of the resulting water must be competitive with fresh water from any other source. Thus, as in most resource problems, the question of economics comes into the picture.

When the water is needed badly enough, cost is of secondary importance. The desalination kits that were part of the equipment provided for the life rafts used in World War II made drinkable—if somewhat less than delicious—fresh water. They were quite expensive, but the people whose lives they helped save could not have cared less about the expense. By the same token, many ships cannot carry adequate supplies of fresh water for an extended voyage, and they have for years employed shipboard desalination by the use of evaporators. Aircraft carriers of the *Forrestal* class, for example, are equipped with salt-water conversion units that turn out 200,000 gallons of fresh water per day. Although practical for these situations, life raft and shipboard techniques would be totally impractical from the economic point of view for solving most of the water-shortage problems on land. It would hardly be worthwhile to raise a $3000-crop when the water to accomplish this cost $4000. For the city of Coalinga, California, on the other hand, the economics were such that desalination of brackish well water was practical. It cost $7.25 per thousand gallons to haul water to the city, and the delivered cost to the consumer was $9.35 per thousand gallons (as opposed to the general cost of about 30 cents per thousand gallons for the average municipality). Coalinga is the first city in the United States to provide its drinking water by desalination of well water; and the cost of $1.45 per thousand gallons, though high, is considerably less than the previous system; hence it is economically feasible. The problem in desalination is not so much how to do it, as how to do it cheaply.

The Office of Saline Water of the U.S. Department of the Interior was established in 1952 to attack the problem of developing practical means for the economic production of fresh water from seawater or other saline waters, such as underground water. Subsequent legislation has bolstered this initial effort. The September 1961 law (Public Law 87-295) authorized an accelerated and expanded program of basic and applied research to the extent of $75 million through fiscal year 1967. The pace has been stepped up, and the possibility of a real breakthrough in this field is quite promising.

There are two basic ways to get fresh water from salt water. The first is to remove the water from the salt, as in distillation or freezing. The second is to remove the salt from the water, as in the process called electrodialysis, which uses a combination of thin membranes and electrical current to filter out the salts. Several desalination pilot plants are currently in operation. These are small research facilities where new techniques are developed and tested, and pilot plants have been established to work on such techniques as distillation, freezing, solar distillation, and the various types of membrane processes. A demonstration plant, as opposed to a pilot plant, is a production unit designed to provide large quantities of fresh water in order to compile data on the engineering, operating, and economic aspects of the system. Through the Office of Saline Water, five demonstration plants are either in operation or in the final stages of construction. One at San Diego, California, produces one million gallons of fresh water per day by what is called the multi-stage flash distillation process. At Freeport, Texas, a demonstration plant using a somewhat different distillation process has been set up. This also puts out about one million gallons of fresh water a day by what is known as the long-tube vertical multiple-effect distillation process. At Wrightville Beach, North Carolina, the freezing process will be tested, and demonstration plants at Webster, South Dakota, and at Roswell, New Mexico, will use underground saline water in an electrodialysis plant and in a plant using what is called the forced-circulation vapor-compression system.

The problem of increasing our supplies of fresh water is now being attacked on several fronts, and the results to date look encouraging. What are needed most right now are new ideas and new techniques, and these are the products of basic and applied research. Fundamental knowledge of the structure of water itself, the behavior of saline solutions, and the movement of ions through membranes can come only through intensive research. The more we can learn about the sea and the complex processes that go on within it, the sooner we will be able to use it more effectively for our own wellbeing. That the development of practical methods for the desalination of seawater is of national and worldwide importance was pointed out by President Kennedy in his special message to the Congress of the United States on February 23, 1961. In discussing natural resources, he said:

"No water resource program is of greater long-range importance— for relief not only of our shortages, but for arid nations the world over—than our efforts to find an effective and economical way to convert water from the world's greatest, cheapest natural resources —the oceans—into water fit for consumption in the home and by industry. Such a break-through would end bitter struggles between neighbors, states, and nations—and bring new hope for millions who live out their lives in dire shortage of usable water and all its physical and economical blessings, though living on the edge of a great body of water throughout their parched life-time."

Food, minerals, and fresh water are probably the three most important commodities that will be extracted from the sea, but its usefulness as a natural resource extends well beyond the efficient recovery of these basic essentials. With increased knowledge of the global sea will come the more effective use of it for commerce and transportation, as a recreational resource, as a source of power through harnessing the tides and the waves, as an environment that is critical to the defense of a nation, as an important element in the long-range prediction or even modification of our weather, and even as a big hole to dump things in. It is indeed a vast resource which holds untold benefits for mankind if it is used wisely. Because it is such a multiple resource, we must be especially careful that in our haste to utilize one particular facet that is needed at the time, we do not jeopardize the eventual utilization of the other facets. For this reason, we must consider the ocean not just as an ore body, or as a food source, or as a repository for our radioactive wastes. We must consider it as one great global natural resource, all of whose parts and processes are intimately interrelated with each other and with the land. The global sea presents to this and to future generations the challenge of new horizons, new frontiers to conquer, a vast area waiting for men to map its buried landscapes, to understand its moving waters, to learn of its abundant and varied life, and finally, armed with this knowledge, to put to the general use of all mankind the many facets of this last great resource on earth.

The International Sea

THE very size and shape of the global sea, washing as it does the shores of many different nations and directly or indirectly affecting the people of all other nations, means that the sea is an international sea. It is owned by no one, yet owned by all. Outside of the various territorial waters, there are no political boundaries. The currents, fish, mineral wealth, and bottom topography know nothing of the fences man likes to put around the things he calls his own, so the high sea is every nation's sea. It is within the international aspect of the global sea that much of our hopes and plans for future survey and research lie, but here also is the source of many existing problems—problems that will become more complex and difficult of solution as the wealth of the seas lures the various countries to extend their control to include these resources.

TERRITORIAL WATERS

Compared to the possible wealth to be recovered from the sea, the amount we now obtain from this resource is relatively small, but already the international lawyers are plagued with a mass of complex problems. This is particularly true in the commercial fishing industry. British naval units are called out to protect British fishing vessels off Iceland, a Japanese fishing vessel is impounded in Alaska, shrimp boats are fired on in the Gulf of Mexico, and the American fishing industry is worried about Soviet trawlers and factory ships on the Grand Banks. Most of these problems stem from the concept of "territorial waters." Just how far out does a coastal state have the right to claim sovereignty? The United States and some other countries have traditionally considered 3 miles to be the limit; others have considered 12 miles to be the limit; still others have arbitrarily set the limits at 4, 5, 9, or 10 miles. Some of the Latin American countries have gone so far as to claim that their territorial waters extend out for 200 miles and to claim exclusive fishing rights within this area.

Obviously such a divergence of national opinions must be settled internationally, and an attempt was made in 1958 during the nine-week International Conference on the Law of the Sea held in Geneva under the auspices of the United Nations. The formal debates and the informal discussions went on far into the night, but no agreement was reached. One proposal for a six-mile territorial sea with an additional contiguous six-mile zone where fisheries rights might be preserved did obtain the approval of the majority of countries, but not of the required two-thirds.

The problem has many ramifications. If, for example, the general three-mile territorial sea became by law a six-mile sea, numerous of the straits through which the high sea now extends would fall within the territorial seas of the countries bordering them. The Strait of Gibraltar is the classic example, but the southern entrance to the Red Sea through the Straits of Bab-al-Mendab is another. This latter would cut off the high-sea approach not only to the Suez Canal, but also to the several countries that border the Red Sea. If the more extensive 12-mile territorial sea were adopted internationally, the Strait of Dover between France and England would be entirely within territorial waters, as would several other straits important to shipping. Among these is the Strait of Hormus, which forms the southern entrance to the Persian Gulf, providing access to Iraq, Kuwait, Saudi Arabia, and various sheikdoms. The 12-mile limit would also remove from international waters the passage between Italy and Corsica, the passages between the 2500 miles of islands in Indonesia from Sumatra to Timor, and the entrance to the Gulf of Finland and to the Gulf of Bothnia, as well as most of the Aegean Sea.

In times of world peace, what is called the "right of innocent passage" through territorial waters is usually honored, and the movements of ships through these straits and passages would be no different from what they are now. But in times of world tension, having these areas within the lawful territorial waters of individual nations rather than as part of the high sea would create additional problems. Aircraft, however, do not enjoy this right of innocent passage, and flying over another nation's territory requires specific agreements. Regardless of the cutting off of the straits and passages to unrestricted air travel, just the seaward extension of a nation's boundaries would create all sorts of problems for air commerce.

The whole problem of the seaward extent of territorial waters will have to be resolved at future international meetings. Other problems that have been dealt with internationally include fishing rights in offshore waters, development of mineral resources on the floor of the sea, laying and maintenance of undersea cables and pipelines, defense interests of coastal nations, and possible pollution of the sea by radioactive waste material. Special international commissions have been established to regulate fishing in certain areas, and others have been set up to regulate fishing for one specific species. These various groups have made honest efforts to come to agreements that will ensure the best utilization of the sea by all nations. Many of their efforts have been highly successful; some have been spectacularly unsuccessful. But only by hammering out international agreements will we ever be able to utilize for the fullest benefit of all people the great resource that is the global sea.

INTERNATIONAL COOPERATION IN OCEANOGRAPHY

The sea is too vast for any one country to undertake all the mapping and all the research and survey work that are needed. Similarly the individual research and survey efforts of the various maritime nations could entail needless duplication of effort if done in an uncoordinated and haphazard way. If, on the other hand, the maritime nations of the world work together with a free exchange of information and plans, and each contributes its part, the job of understanding the ocean and utilizing its resources for all mankind will be accomplished sooner and with considerably less effort and expense.

Recognizing that the study of the sea should indeed be an international venture, and that there was a need for dynamic and coordinated international action to carry out such a venture, there was formed within the United Nations Educational, Scientific, and Cultural Organization (UNESCO) an Intergovernmental Oceanographic Commission. Some 44 countries were represented at the first IOC meeting held in Paris in October of 1961. The effectiveness of this organization rests in the fact that it is "intergovernmental" rather than just "international." The distinction lies in the fact that the oceanographers at this meeting spoke not just as scientists, but as official spokesmen for their governments. Oceanography is such an expensive science—because ships and ship operations are expensive—that it must be primarily a government-supported effort. In the past, oceanographers had attended international meetings, but always as individuals. The level of international cooperation needed to be extended to dealings between governments.

Interestingly enough, intergovernmental cooperation seems to be working. Agreements are being reached on the almost unrestricted exchange of oceanographic data, on communications and navigational aids, on the wider use of fixed stations such as lightships and buoys for obtaining oceanographic data, on the coordination of national and regional programs at sea, and—most important—on cooperative programs for oceanographic survey and research work. An example of this last is the International Cooperative Investigations of the Tropical Atlantic. Starting in February of 1963, oceanographic ships from seven countries, including the United States, converged on the tropical Atlantic. In a carefully worked-out program, each ship took one specific part of the equatorial Atlantic in an area stretching from South America to Africa. During a two-week period, each ship made the same measurements along a series of north-south lines across the Equator to get for the first time an almost photographic picture of a large section of the ocean—a synoptic survey. The problem in the past has been that the things you are trying to measure—water temperature, currents, salinity, dissolved oxygen concentration, animal abundances, and the like—all vary so rapidly with time that it is difficult to make sense from the observations made by a single ship covering a large area over a long period of time. It is hard to distinguish between changes with time and changes from place to place. The synoptic survey is one answer to this problem, and the first large-scale synoptic survey ever tried on the international scale is this Tropical Atlantic Investigation sponsored by the Intergovernmental Oceanographic Commission.

The International Indian Ocean Expedition, now under the sponsorship of the IOC, is another international cooperative investigation. This is not a synoptic survey—that is, the ships are not all there at the same time working on the same observations—but it has resulted in the various maritime nations of the world concentrating at least a part of their oceanographic effort toward the exploration and understanding of the least-known major arm of the global sea. This international effort will continue for a number of years, and analysis of the results and publication of the atlases and professional papers will take many more years.

The challenge of the global sea is there. It needs only the intrepid men with the love of adventure and the curiosity to find new information and the imagination to propose new theories based on these facts, and then go back to sea to test these theories. The global sea is fascinating in all its aspects, and the pursuit of its secrets has fascinated men in the past. It provides men today with the thrill of new discoveries. To the man of tomorrow it will present the opportunity to contribute to the development of the last great resource on earth. The land and the sea are intimately related, and the future of mankind on land to a very real degree depends upon his global sea.

Bibliography

Brynielsson, H. (Chairman), *Radioactive-Waste Disposal into the Sea,* Report of the *ad hoc* Panel, Safety Series No. 5, International Atomic Energy Agency, Vienna, 1961

Carritt, D. E. (Chairman), *Desalination Research and the Water Problem,* Pub. 901, National Academy of Sciences-National Research Council, Washington, D.C., 1962

Coker, R. D., *This Great and Wide Sea,* University of North Carolina Press, Chapel Hill, 1947

Daugherty, C. M., *Searchers of the Sea: Pioneers in Oceanography,* The Viking Press, New York, 1961

Defant, A., *Ebb and Flow: The Tides of Earth, Air, and Water,* University of Michigan Press, Ann Arbor, 1958

Hardy, A. C., *The Open Sea, Its Natural History, The World of Plankton,* Houghton, Mifflin Co., Boston, 1959

Herdman, W. A., *Founders of Oceanography and Their Work,* Edwin Arnold and Co., London, 1923

Shepard, F. P., *Submarine Geology,* Harper and Brothers, New York, 1948

Shepard, F. P., *The Earth Beneath the Sea,* Johns Hopkins University Press, Baltimore, 1959

Stommel, H., *The Gulf Stream,* University of California Press, Berkeley, 1958

Sverdrup, H. U., Johnson, M. W., and Fleming, R. H., *The Oceans, Their Physics, Chemistry, and General Biology,* Prentice-Hall, Inc., Englewood Cliffs, New Jersey, 1942

Tressler, D. K., and Lemon, J. McW., *Marine Products of Commerce,* 2nd ed., Reinhold Publishing Corp., New York, 1951

Von Arx, W. S., *An Introduction to Physical Oceanography,* Addison-Wesley Publishing Co., Inc., Reading, Massachusetts, 1962

Index

DATE DUE

NO 5 70			
GAYLORD			PRINTED IN U.S.A.